100
SCIENCE
LESSONS

YEAR R
Scottish Primary 1

Published by Scholastic Ltd,
Villiers House,
Clarendon Avenue,
Leamington Spa,
Warwickshire CV32 5PR
Printed by Bell & Bain Ltd, Glasgow

567890   567890

Series Consultant
Peter Riley

Author
Georgie Beasley

Editor
Joel Lane

Assistant Editor
David Sandford

Series Designers
David Hurley
Joy Monkhouse

Designers
Paul Cheshire
Sarah Rock

Cover photography
Martyn Chillmaid

Illustrations
Colin Shelbourn

British Library Cataloguing-in-Publication Data
A catalogue record for this book is available from the British Library.

ISBN 0-439-01801-3

Teachers should consult their own school policies and guidelines concerning practical work and participation of children in scientific experiments. You should only select activities which you feel can be carried out safely and confidently in the classroom.

Acknowledgements
Qualifications and Curriculum Authority for the use of extracts from the QCA/DfEE document *Curriculum Guidance for the Foundation Stage* ©2000 Qualifications and Curriculum Authority.
The National Curriculum for Wales 2000
© The Queens Printer and Controller of HMSO. Reproduced under the terms of HMSO Guidance Note 10.
Extracts from:
The National Curriculum for Northern Ireland 2000.
5–14 Curriculum for Scotland.

Contents

Introduction

100 Science Lessons is a series of year-specific teachers' resource books that provide a wealth of lesson plans and photocopiable resources for delivering a whole year of science teaching, including differentiation and assessment. Where relevant, the series follows the QCA *Science Scheme of Work* in the sequencing of topics in the primary years.

However, instead of having six or seven units as in the QCA scheme, the book for each year (including Year R/Primary 1) contains eight units. These units are the familiar topics: 1. Ourselves, 2. Animals & plants, 3. The environment, 4. Materials, 5. Electricity, 6. Forces & motion, 7. Light & sound, 8. Earth & beyond. They appear in the same order in every book, but have sub-titles that describe the emphasis of the work in that year. For example, in this book Unit 1 is Ourselves: This is me! and Unit 6 is Forces and motion: Pushing and pulling.

By having eight units, this resource provides a foundation for the National Curriculum and QCA *Science Scheme of Work* in England, and accommodates preparation for the demands of the curricula for Wales, Scotland and Northern Ireland. The series creates opportunities to visit each topic in every year: in the primary years, after visiting a topic in synchrony with the QCA Scheme (for example), you can make a further visit the following year for extension or consolidation of the previous year's work.

Each unit (or section of a longer unit) is divided into a number of lessons, ending with an assessment lesson. The organisation grid at the start of each unit shows the objectives and outcomes of each lesson, and gives a quick overview of the lesson content (Main activity, Group activities, Plenary). The Early Learning Goals for the Foundation Stage for England, Wales, Scotland and Northern Ireland in knowledge and understanding of the world (links to which are given on pages 190–191) provide the basis for the lesson objectives used throughout the book.

ORGANISATION (19 LESSONS)

	OBJECTIVES	MAIN ACTIVITY	GROUP ACTIVITIES	PLENARY	OUTCOMES
LESSON 1	• To develop sorting skills by looking carefully.	Sort a variety of fruits by colour, shape and size.	Look closely at the inside of fruits. Make fruit prints. Identify fruit segments. Set up a fruit shop.	Talk about the patterns made by the fruit prints.	• Can sort a range of fruits by colour, shape and size by looking closely. • Can sort fruits using other criteria.
LESSON 2	• To develop sorting skills by touching and feeling. • To develop an idea of texture.	Talk about the textures of different fruits, developing vocabulary to describe them.	Sort fruits by texture. Make a fruit salad. Structured role-play in fruit shop.	Talk about the changes in the fruit when the fruit salad is made.	• Can find out about fruit by touching and feeling. • Can compare fruit before and after peeling, noting similarities and differences.

LESSON PLANS

A context for each set of lessons is suggested. This provides a theme for the planning and organisation of appropriate play activities through which very young children learn, and is in keeping with the ethos of the curriculum for the Foundation Stage.

Each lesson plan is divided into four parts: Introduction, Main activity, Group activities and Plenary session. In many of the lessons, the introduction is supported by a vocabulary list that will help in delivering the lesson and support assessment of the work. The introduction sets the scene for the lesson and starts with a practical context such as going for walk, listening to a story or singing a favourite song. The Main activity features direct whole-class or group teaching, and may include instructions on how to gain the children's attention, stimulate their interest and increase their motivation. Guidance on the type of questions to ask is also given; these will allow the teacher to assess the children's knowledge and understanding prior to the Group activities, and to develop new vocabulary associated with the learning objectives.

There is then a choice of several activities to engage groups of children. These activities are cross-curricular; those that are intended to develop skills in scientific enquiry require focused teaching and support from an adult. Those that are play activities have been designed so that the children can explore independently, but retain a very tight link to the Main activity. Advice on differentiation and formative assessment linked to this work is provided. Finally, there are details of a plenary session; this is often related to the independent activities, allowing you to monitor what the children have learned.

About 60% of the lesson plans in this book, including those for the assessment lessons, are presented in full detail. Many of these are followed by outlines for closely related lessons on the same topics or concepts, using the same background ideas. To avoid repetition and allow you to focus on the essentials of the lesson, these plans are presented as grids for you to develop. They contain the major features of the detailed lesson plans, allowing you to plan for progression and assessment.

Detailed lesson plans
The lessons in this book have been designed to encourage and develop the children's investigative skills. Children at this stage are not expected to carry out a complete investigation or to develop enquiry skills without a great deal of help. Although many will not be able to set up a fair test, a few may be able to recognise when a test is not fair; it is important that these children begin to understand the process and practise the skills of making predictions, planning a fair test, choosing appropriate resources, collecting data and drawing conclusions. This process forms part of the Differentiation section for more able children in many lessons. Even lessons that focus on knowledge and understanding are approached in an investigative way through questioning (in order to develop the children's thinking skills) and through observation and recording of what happens (in order to develop their ability to notice how things change). Opportunities to develop the skill of prediction are included in many lessons – though you should be prepared for young children not wanting to be proved wrong. Many will stick stubbornly to their prediction, despite the results of the test indicating otherwise.

Context
The lessons in each unit of work are grouped by content. The context suggested for each set of lessons provides the opportunity to teach this aspect of knowledge and understanding of the world through play activities. For example, the resources used to teach the children about materials are found in the role-play area, sand-pit and water tray, while the lessons to teach about the Earth and beyond are developed through the process of setting up a series of displays.

Objectives
The objectives of the lessons are derived from the statements in the curriculum for the Foundation stage. They are stated in a way that helps to focus each lesson plan and give a unique theme to each unit. At least one objective for each lesson is related to content knowledge, and there may be one or more objectives relating to scientific enquiry. You may choose to replace these with others to meet your needs and the skills you wish the children to develop.

Resources and Preparation
The Resources section provides a list of everything you will need in order to deliver the lesson, including any of the photocopiables in this book. Preparation describes anything that needs to be done in advance of the lesson, such as making a game, preparing a display, organising a visit, teaching a song or carrying out a risk assessment. As part of the preparation for all practical work, you should consult your school's policies concerning the use of plants and animals in the

classroom so that you can select activities for which you are confident to take responsibility. The ASE publication *Be Safe!* gives useful guidance on what things are safe to use in the classroom.

Vocabulary

Each fully detailed lesson plan has an associated vocabulary list containing words that should be used by the children in discussing and presenting their work, and in their writing. The words relate both to scientific enquiry and to knowledge and understanding.

It is important that the children develop their scientific vocabulary in order to describe their findings and observations and to explain their ideas. Whenever a specialist word is used, it should be accompanied by a definition, as some children in the class may take time to understand and differentiate the meanings of words such as 'environment', 'waterproof' and 'mix'.

Introduction

The lesson introductions contain ideas to get each lesson started and to 'set the scene'. You may also wish to draw on the background information presented in the Context, or to make links with other lessons in your scheme of work.

Main teaching activity

This section presents a direct, whole-class (or occasionally group) teaching session to follow the introduction. This will help you to deliver the content knowledge outlined in the lesson objectives to the children before they start their group work. The notes may include guidance on discussion, or on performing one or more demonstrations or class sorting activities to help the children understand the work ahead.

The relative proportions of the lesson given to the Introduction, Main teaching activity and Group activities vary. If you are reminding the children of their previous work and getting them on to their own investigations, the group activities may dominate the lesson time; if you are introducing a new topic or concept, you may wish to spend most of the lesson engaged in whole-class teaching.

Group activities

The Group activities are very flexible. Some may be best-suited to individual work, while others may be suitable for work in pairs or larger groupings. In the detailed lesson plans, there are usually about four Group activities provided for each lesson. Two are focused activities that require the support of an adult to reinforce the learning in the Main teaching activity; two are play activities that the children can access independently to explore aspects of the learning objective. For example, in a lesson about mixing materials, a table is organised for the children to explore a range of materials that do not mix with water. Some further activities can be tried by children who complete the initial practical tasks successfully and quickly. Some of the Group activities are supported by a photocopiable sheet. Group activities whose context is play are indicated by a small bear icon.

The Group activities may include some writing. These activities are also aimed at strengthening the children's science literacy and supporting their English literacy skills. They may involve writing labels and captions, developing scientific vocabulary, writing about investigations or recording results, presenting data, explaining what they have observed, or using appropriate secondary sources. The children's mathematical skills are also developed through number and data handling work in the context of science investigations.

Differentiation

For each of the lessons, where appropriate, there are suggestions for differentiated work for the more able and less able children in the class. Differentiated Group activities are designed so that all the children who perform these tasks can make a contribution to the Plenary session. At this stage many of the activities are suitable for all abilities, with children contributing at their own level.

Assessment

Each lesson includes advice on how to assess the children's success in the activities against the lesson objectives. This may include questions to ask or observations to make to help you build up a picture of the children's developing ideas and plan future lessons. A separate summative assessment lesson is provided at the end of each section of work. Where a longer unit divides into distinct content areas (in Unit 7, for example), a summative assessment lesson has also been provided part-way through the unit.

Plenary

This is a very important part of the lesson. It is important not to let it get squeezed out by mistiming other activities in the lesson. Suggestions are given for drawing the various strands of the lesson together in this session. If an investigation has been tried, the work of different groups can be compared and evaluated. The scene may be set for another lesson, or the lesson objectives and outcomes may be reviewed.

On occasions, small tasks may be suggested for the children to do at home. These are tasks, such as collecting things to add to a class display or observing the Moon, that cannot easily be done in school time.

Lesson outcomes

These are statements related to the lesson objectives, expanding on them to describe what the children should have achieved through the lesson.

Links

Between units: The lesson may be linked to other units or lessons elsewhere in the book to provide progression or reinforcement. You may like to consider these links in planning your scheme of work – for example, linking Unit 5, Lesson 4 (identifying a range of household electrical appliances that give light) with Unit 7, Lesson 5 (collecting things that give light).

Across the curriculum: Many links are made to personal, social and emotional development and focus on the way that young children learn through co-operation, taking turns and sharing resources. There are also links to content and skills in subjects such as language and literacy and mathematical development. Great emphasis is placed on communication skills and links to other aspects of knowledge and understanding of the world, such as designing and making in technology and a growing awareness of their immediate surroundings in geography. Links to the use of ICT in the classroom are also made where appropriate.

Lesson plan grids

These short lesson plans, presented in the form of a grid, offer further activity ideas to broaden the topic coverage. As the example below shows, they have the same basic structure as the detailed lesson plans. They lack the Preparation, Introduction, Vocabulary and Links sections, but these are supported by the related detailed lesson plans. Notes suggesting a Main activity and Group activities are provided for you to develop. There are usually no photocopiables linked to these lesson plans.

LESSON 3

Objective	● To develop sorting skills by using the sense of smell.
Resources	A collection of fruits including an orange, a banana, an apple and a strawberry (other fruits with a distinctive and easily recognisable scent will do), each chopped up into a disposable cup with a paper cover held on with an elastic band.

Main activity	Talk to the children about how we smell things. Make sure they understand that we use our noses to smell. Emphasise the importance of not smelling things we are unfamiliar with: it might be dangerous. It is safe to do so in this lesson, because they will only be smelling familiar fruit to try and guess what is in each pot.
	    One at a time, pass the cups around the class and ask the children to guess what fruit is in each cup. Invite those who can to describe the smell, using words such as 'sweet' and 'tangy'. They could also use words and phrases related to the names of fruits, such as 'orangey' or 'like a pineapple'. (This is difficult for very young children, however, and is not essential.) As each cup returns to you, remove the paper cover and pass the cup around again so that the children can see whether they were right.
	    Set up a similar Group activity, using different fruits, for some of the children to play during the day.

Differentiation	Less able children, and those who are still unfamiliar with the names of the fruits, may need to repeat the activity in smaller groups with an adult. Ask more able children to make their own pots (under supervision), containing different fruits for their friends to guess.
Assessment	Invite the children to record by drawing the fruits that they think are in each pot. Keep these drawings as evidence of the children's ability to use their sense of smell to identify fruit.
Plenary	Share the fruit salad and talk about the different smells of the fruits. Remind the children of the names of the different fruits.
Outcomes	● Can link the sense of smell to the nose. ● Can identify fruit by using the sense of smell.

RESOURCES
Photocopiable sheets

These are an integral part of many of the lessons and are found at the end of the relevant unit, marked with the 'photocopiable' symbol. They may provide resources, means of recording (including collage, writing or drawing) or activities (such as matching and sequencing).

Classroom equipment and space

A wide range of resources are needed for the lessons in this book. However, every attempt has been made to restrict the list to resources that will be readily available in most Year R/Primary 1 classrooms. Each lesson plan includes a resources list. When you have planned which lessons you wish to use, you could make up your own resources list for the term's or year's work. Encourage your colleagues to do the same for other years, so that you can compare lists, identify times when there may be a high demand for particular resources and make adjustments as necessary.

ICT

Many of the lessons in this book can be enhanced by the use of ICT. As new products are entering the market all the time, few are specified in this book. However, you may like to plan your ICT work under these headings:

Interactive programs

These are available for the youngest children in the school, and some are useful to reinforce early skills with older children:
● *My World* series from Semerc (includes *All About Ourselves*, *Skeleton* and *Healthy Eating*)
● *My Amazing Human Body* from Dorling Kindersley.

Information retrieval

Some children may be starting to find information from secondary sources, including CD-ROMs. Where this is the case, it is important that the children have a focus for their enquiries, that the materials offered are at an appropriate level, and that the task of information retrieval is sufficiently challenging.

Visual recordings

A visual record of an investigation may be made by taking photographs (with a conventional or digital camera) or recording an activity with a video camera and storing the information on the computer for use in a presentation. Visual recordings should be annotated to provide a complete record, not just a picture of the children's experiences.

Desktop publishing

Some children may be able to design and produce booklets of their work using their own written material, graphs, charts, photographs and information retrieved from other sources.

Presentations

Presentations may be made using video sequences that have been recorded during an investigation with a digital or video camera.

ASSESSMENT

The assessments in this book indicate the likely progress of children in Year R/Primary 1. The statements relate specifically to work in this book, and are arranged in groups to reflect different levels. In this year's work, it is expected that most children will achieve the Early Learning Goals in England or their equivalents in other areas of the UK. Some may be working towards NC Level 1/Scottish Level A, but some may not progress so well and may be working towards achieving the national goals for ages 3–5. In the Early Learning Goals in England, the 'stepping stones' are highlighted in the QCA file in a different colour band for easy reference.

You may find it useful to determine what the children already know before embarking on each unit. If appropriate, talk to adults at the pre-school settings attended by the children previously and find out what work has been covered. Talk to the children about what they know, and use the results to plan differentiated activities and provide materials as you teach the unit.

The last lesson in every unit (or section of a longer unit) focuses on summative assessment. This assessment samples the content of the unit, focusing on its key theme(s); its results should be used in conjunction with other assessments that you have made during the teaching of the unit. The lesson comprises several activities that may take the form of photocopiable sheets, 'question and answer' sessions or practical activities. This will give you an idea of how the children are progressing relative to the Early Learning Goals. You may wish to start these lessons by reviewing the vocabulary learned in the unit.

A sample of the children's work from the assessment and other lessons in this book, kept in a general portfolio, will be very useful in supporting your teacher assessment judgments.

SUPPORT FOR PLANNING

Developing your scheme of work

This book is planned to support the national goals for achievement at ages 3–5. In England, for example, these goals are given by the QCA *Curriculum Guidance for the Foundation Stage – Knowledge and Understanding of the World*. In planning your school scheme of work, you may wish to look at the units in this book or throughout the series along with those of the national curriculum (and the QCA *Science Scheme of Work* for Year 1 in England), towards which the children will be working. You may also wish to address the objectives in your curriculum planning more directly to those of the curriculum documents.

The information on pages 190–191 shows how the statements of desirable attainment at age 5 in knowledge and understanding and scientific enquiry for England, Wales, Scotland and Northern Ireland provide the basis for the lesson objectives used throughout the eight units in this book. In the grids, each statement is cross-referenced to one or more lessons to help with curriculum planning.

Planning progression

The Series topic map on page 192 shows the focus of each of the units in the books in this series, to help you work out your plan of progression. By looking at this chart, the chart of curriculum coverage on pages 190–191 and the organisation chart for each unit, you can plan for progression through the year and from one year to the next, covering the whole of the work needed for Year R and Key Stages 1 and 2/ Primary 1–7.

You may choose to use all or most of the lessons from the units in this book, or make a selection to provide a 'backbone' for your own curriculum planning and supplement it with lessons you have already found successful from other sources. The pages in this book are perforated and hole-punched, so you can separate them and put them in a planning file with other favourite activities and worksheets.

TEACHING SCIENCE IN YEAR R/PRIMARY 1

The units in this book introduce children to work on knowledge and understanding of the world, building on the early learning work done in pre-school settings. It is expected that most children will attain the Early Learning Goals as they work through this book, though some may still be working towards these and others may be working towards Level 1/Level A in some areas.

An underlying theme of this book is the application of science knowledge to our everyday world. As the children are maturing, this approach allows them to consider the ways in which science can alter our everyday life. This should help them see that it is important to know about science (to become scientifically literate) and to form opinions that, in future, can help in the sensible development of their world. This idea is only touched upon in this book, but should help to prepare the children for work on this topic in later years.

A brief description of the unit contents follows, to show more specifically how the themes are developed:

● **Unit 1: Ourselves** focuses directly on the children themselves. Subtitled 'This is me!', the unit develops a knowledge and understanding of the parts of the body, the way we move, the ways in which we change as we grow and the importance of keeping ourselves safe. The main focus is on developing observation skills through exploration using the senses.

● **Unit 2: Animals & plants** focuses on 'Looking at animals and plants'. The children learn to recognise and name some common animals and their main external parts, and learn how they move. They also learn to recognise and name some common plants, know the main parts of plants, know that most plants grow from seeds and know that plants need water to survive. They begin to understand the importance of plants as a food source. Again, the focus is on developing observation and sorting skills through exploration using the senses.

● **Unit 3: The environment**, subtitled 'Out and about', looks at the children's immediate surroundings and stresses the importance of caring for them because they provide the habitats of plants and animals. The children will learn how to care for living things indoors as well.

● **Unit 4: Materials** focuses on 'Exploring materials' and finding ways to identify some common materials. It looks at the range of materials in the environment and their different uses. The children learn to sort materials by some of their simple properties. They explore how some materials mix with water and others do not.

● **Unit 5: Electricity** focuses on 'Making things work'. The children consider how we use electricity, where it can be found around us and some of the dangers it presents. The work includes the identification of appliances, toys and other devices that use mains electricity and batteries.

● **Unit 6: Forces & motion** focuses on 'Pushing and pulling'. The children use a range of toys and other everyday objects to explore the effects of pushing and pulling. The skill of prediction is introduced in this unit.

● **Unit 7: Light & sound** focuses on 'Looking and listening'. The children learn to identify various light and sound sources, and learn about using light and sound to keep safe. They make a dark place and investigate what they can see in it by playing a range of games. They find out what happens to paint when colours are mixed together and mixed with white and black. They make sounds in a variety of ways and investigate how high, low, loud and quiet sounds are made.

● **Unit 8: Earth & beyond** focuses on looking 'Up in the sky'. The children explore what they can see during the day and at night. They distinguish between things that are only seen in the sky (such as the Sun and Moon) and things that can also be seen on the ground (such as birds and aeroplanes). They also consider where light comes from during the day and at night.

This is me!

ORGANISATION (19 LESSONS)

	OBJECTIVES	MAIN ACTIVITY	GROUP ACTIVITIES	PLENARY	OUTCOMES
LESSON 1	● To develop sorting skills by looking carefully.	Sort a variety of fruits by colour, shape and size.	Look closely at the inside of fruits. Make fruit prints. Identify fruit segments. Set up a fruit shop.	Talk about the patterns made by the fruit prints.	● Can sort a range of fruits by colour, shape and size by looking closely. ● Can sort fruits using other criteria.
LESSON 2	● To develop sorting skills by touching and feeling. ● To develop an idea of texture.	Talk about the textures of different fruits, developing vocabulary to describe them.	Sort fruits by texture. Make a fruit salad. Structured role-play in fruit shop.	Talk about the changes in the fruit when the fruit salad is made.	● Can find out about fruit by touching and feeling. ● Can compare fruit before and after peeling, noting similarities and differences.
LESSON 3	● To develop sorting skills by using the sense of smell.	Explore a variety of fruits using the sense of smell, developing the vocabulary to describe them.		Share a fruit salad and talk about the different smells.	● Can link the sense of smell to the nose. ● Can identify fruit by using the sense of smell.
LESSON 4	● To develop sorting skills by using the sense of taste.	Identify fruits by tasting, developing the vocabulary to describe them.		Share a fruit salad and talk about the different tastes.	● Can use the sense of taste to find out about fruit. ● Can link the sense of taste to the tongue and mouth.
LESSON 5	● To know that we need to drink to stay alive. ● To develop recording skills through sorting.	Make a list of favourite drinks.	Relate the names of fruit drinks to pictures of fruits. Identify drinks that need to have water added. Get water ready to drink.	Talk about the importance of drinking healthy drinks.	● Know that they need to drink to stay alive. ● Know that thirst is the body's way of saying 'Give me a drink'. ● Can begin to organise information in graphical form.
LESSON 6	● To learn that not all things are safe to touch, smell and taste.	Look for and examining 'danger' signs on empty cartons.	Add 'Do not touch' stickers to containers. Sort pictures of materials into 'safe' and 'not safe'. Identify 'danger' signs.	Look at cleaning materials and talk about their safety.	● Begin to learn how to keep themselves safe by knowing that not all things are safe to touch, smell and taste.
LESSON 7	● To learn which parts of the body are used to smell, touch, see, hear and taste.	Match the senses to pictures of a nose, hand, eye, ear and tongue. Label these body parts.		Reinforce safety issues relating to touches, smells and tastes. Talk about dangers to ears and eyes.	● Know which parts of the body we use to hear, see, smell and taste, and which main parts we use to feel and touch. ● Have begun to think about how to look after our bodies and protect our hearing and sight.
LESSON 8	● To learn that we can use our fingers and hands to touch and feel, and that we can use this sense to identify objects. ● To explore and describe a range of objects that have different shapes and textures.	Feely bag activity: identifying an object by its shape and texture.	Feely bag activity. Record what they think they have touched. Print with objects of different textures.	Match the texture prints to the objects. Make a display of prints and objects.	● Can identify objects by feeling their shape and texture. ● Can describe similarities and differences between objects. ● Can talk about the materials from which different objects are made.

ORGANISATION (19 LESSONS)

	OBJECTIVES	MAIN ACTIVITY	GROUP ACTIVITIES	PLENARY	OUTCOMES
LESSON 9	● To learn to identify objects from the sounds they make.	Feely bag activity: identifying an object from the sound that it makes.	Identify recorded sounds. Share a book with sound effects. Find pictures of things that make a sound. Play with percussion instruments.	Add sound effects to a familiar story.	● Know that they use their ears to hear. ● Can recognise familiar objects from the sounds they make.
LESSON 10	● To begin to use their senses to identify similarities and differences.	Compare sound pots. Play a dominoes game with textures.	Repeat the 'texture dominoes' game. Match pairs of sound pots.	Play either game together, talking about the textures or sounds.	● Can begin to use more than one sense to explore a range of objects and to identify similarities and differences.

	OBJECTIVES		ACTIVITIES 1 and 2	OUTCOME
ASSESSMENT 11	● To assess the children's ability to explore using all five senses and to identify familiar objects. ● To reinforce the use of drawing to record findings in an investigation.		Use the senses to find out what is inside different parcels. Identify food items using only the sense of taste.	● Can explore a range of familiar objects using their senses.

	OBJECTIVES	MAIN ACTIVITY	GROUP ACTIVITIES	PLENARY	OUTCOMES
LESSON 12	● To recognise and learn the names of parts of the body and be able to say what they are used for.	Learn songs to teach the parts of the body.	Make and solve body jigsaws. Fix 'people' jigsaws. Label body parts on a picture. Paint and label pictures of themselves.	Sing songs and rhymes about the parts of the body, with actions.	● Can identify some external parts of the human body and recognise their names. ● Can talk about what they are doing.
LESSON 13	● To learn that we use different parts of our bodies to move in different ways.	Explore which body parts are used for moving in a PE lesson. Draw pictures of all the ways they moved.		Talk about all the ways the children moved and make a display with the pictures.	● Know that we can move in many different ways, using different parts of our bodies and sometimes more than one part at a time.
LESSON 14	● To know that we all grow and change as we get older.	Look at photographs of the same person as a baby and as an adult. Compare the ways a baby and a toddler move.	Compare early and recent photographs of themselves. Look at baby clothes and toys. Match baby clothes to children's clothes. Sort baby clothes by type of item.	Make a display of the clothes and toys, reinforcing how we change as we grow older.	● Can sort and match items of clothing of very different sizes and explain how they would have fitted everyone at a certain stage in their life. ● Know that we all change as we grow older.
LESSON 15	● To learn that we can all do many things for ourselves.	Talk to an adult visitor about care of a baby. List the things a baby can do and things the children can do. Create parts of the display.		Make a display of faces and speech bubbles to show what a baby can do and what the children can do.	● Know what babies are and are not able to do for themselves. ● Understand that as young children get older, they are able to do more things for themselves.
LESSON 16	● To investigate similarities and differences between us.	Discuss the physical similarities and differences between two children.	Paint pictures of themselves. Play 'Spot the difference'. Play a 'Who am I describing?' game. Make a faces collage. Make handprints and footprints.	Ask the children to identify the subjects of some of their paintings.	● Know that we all have things about us that are the same and things that are different. ● Can investigate similarities and differences through first-hand experience.
LESSON 17	● To know that people come in different shapes and sizes. ● To begin to order things according to size. ● To begin to match objects and people according to size.	Compare the sizes of items in the context of the 'Three bears' story.	Make beds for the three bears. Order soft toys by size. Make the three bears' cottage in the role-play area. Make the three bears' beds.	Talk about the different sizes of things in the three bears' cottage.	● Know the comparative language of size. ● Can sort and match items according to size. ● Have begun to classify things according to size.

ORGANISATION (19 LESSONS)

	OBJECTIVES	MAIN ACTIVITY	GROUP ACTIVITIES	PLENARY	OUTCOMES
LESSON 18	● To learn that we all grow. ● To find out who are the tallest and shortest children in the class.	Compare the children's heights. The children paint life-sized pictures of each other.		Organise the children into height order.	● Know that we all grow. ● Know that some people grow taller than others. ● Know that some people grow faster than others. ● Know that we are all different heights.

	OBJECTIVES	MAIN ACTIVITY	ACTIVITIES 2 and 3	OUTCOMES
ASSESSMENT 19	● To find out how many parts of the body the children can name. ● To assess whether the children understand that we all grow and change as we become older. ● To assess whether the children can identify simple similarities and differences between people.	Match labels to the correct body parts on the computer.	Order a set of pictures to show a person getting older. Draw pictures of themselves as babies and as they look now.	● Investigate fruit and other objects using all five senses. ● Find out, recognise and identify some of the features of humans. ● Understand the changes that occur in humans as we get older. ● Look closely at similarities and differences between human beings.

Context: MAKING A FRUIT SALAD

Lessons 1–5 of this unit are set in the context of making a fruit salad, and can be taught as a daily activity through the week. Lesson 6 goes on to look at hazardous substances that should not be touched, smelt or tasted. The activities can be included in a food topic, a healthy eating project and/or the making of a fruit shop role-play area. The children will be taught to explore the use of their senses through play activities, thus developing the early investigative skills of noticing similarities and differences and using them to sort and record. These ideas can be adapted for other food preparation activities, such as making sandwiches or vegetable fingers.

LESSON 1

OBJECTIVE

● To develop sorting skills by looking carefully.

RESOURCES

Main teaching activity: A collection of fruit (enough to make a fruit salad for the children to share at snack time), including banana, pineapple, green and red apple, green and black grapes, pear, orange, kiwi fruit, peach and plum; a tablecloth; cardboard labels and a marker pen (optional); a large bowl.

Group activities: 1. A cutting board, a knife, sorting rings. **2.** Green, red, yellow and orange paint, A3 paper. **3.** Photocopiable page 35, pencils. **4.** Play fruit, baskets, a table and tablecloth, magazines with pictures of fruit (or labels from tinned fruit), A3 paper, adhesive. For the extension task, include a lemon, lime, grapefruit, tangerine, pomegranate, passion fruit and dried fruits.

Vocabulary
pips, seeds, core, segments, peel, flesh, juice

PREPARATION

Choose types of fruit that look different in a number of ways: different shapes, colours, stems, peel and so on. Organise the tables for the focused Group activities. Spread the tablecloth in the centre of a carpeted area or over a fairly large table. Organise the fruit and sorting rings in the centre, so that the children can see all the resources. Make enough copies of photocopiable page 35. Cut up some fruit into pieces (large enough for the children to handle) and put them in a large bowl to share at the end of the lesson.

INTRODUCTION

Sit the children around the tablecloth. Show them the collection of fruit. Ask whether anyone can tell you the name of any of these fruits. Can they tell you the name of the kiwi fruit, pineapple and pear? Tell them the names of all the fruits.

MAIN TEACHING ACTIVITY

Hold up the orange and ask the children to give you one word that describes what the orange looks like. Prompt them to mention the shape or the colour. Can they hold the orange in their hand so that it cannot be seen? Repeat this activity with the banana and one of the apples.

Ask the children whether they can put any of the fruits together because they are the same colour. Put all the yellow fruits together, then the red, the green and so on, using the set rings. Now sort the fruits by size and by shape. Explain that you are sorting them into sets. You may wish to label the sets at this point. Tell the children that they have been using their sense of sight to sort the fruits, looking carefully to see the differences.

GROUP ACTIVITIES

1. With a group of six to eight children, cut the different fruits open one at a time and talk about what is inside. Discuss the peel, flesh, core and seeds. Tell the children that the seeds are called 'pips' in apples, pears, oranges and grapes, and 'stones' in plums and peaches. *Which is the juiciest fruit? How do you know? Can you see the juice?* Sort the fruits into sets by the colour of the pips, the appearance of the flesh, and whether or not we eat the peel.
2. With an adult helper, invite another group of four to six children to make fruit prints. This could be set in the context of making a frieze for the role-play area. Ask the helper to cut an apple, an orange and a banana horizontally across the centre, showing the shapes of the cross-sections and the star shape of the apple core. Let the children use green, red, yellow and orange paint to print fruit patterns, matching the colour of the paint to the colour of each fruit's peel.
3. Give the children a copy each of page 35. Ask them to draw lines matching each whole fruit to a segment or slice in the bowl. Ask questions such as: *How can you recognise a segment of an orange? What do the kiwi fruit slices look like?*
4. Ask an adult helper to set up a fruit shop in the role-play area. Ask the less able children to sort the play fruits into baskets: one for each kind of fruit. Invite them to find pictures in magazines, or collect labels from tinned fruit to decorate their baskets and make posters for the shop.

DIFFERENTIATION

Introduce more exotic fruits to the more able children, such as a pomegranate, star fruit and passion fruit. They could repeat the Group activities with these fruits, and group fruits of the same general type (such as citrus fruits or berries) together. You could also present some dried fruits and explain what these fruits were before they were dried.

Give the less able children further daily opportunities to sort fruits using their sense of sight, reinforcing the vocabulary. Focus on different shapes, sizes and especially colours.

ASSESSMENT

Watch the children as they sort the fruit, and note those children who take the lead. Reorganise the groups to bring together the children not taking the lead, to see whether they are now able to complete the activity unaided.

PLENARY

Ask the children who took part in the fruit-printing activity to talk about the shapes they have made and the colours they have used. Do other children notice the star shape in the centre of the apple print and the shape of the orange segments? *Are all the printed shapes circles? Which ones are? Would all the fruit prints be circles if they were cut across the middle?*

Share the fruit salad by passing around the bowl and letting each child take a piece.

OUTCOMES

● Can sort a range of fruits by colour, shape and size by looking closely.
● (More able children) Can sort fruits by more complex criteria, such as whether they are citrus fruits or whether they have stones or pips.

LINKS

Across the curriculum: the skill of exploring using their senses is fundamental to the children's early learning in many areas of the under-fives curriculum. The printing activity is closely related to creative development, developing fine motor skills and physical development. The fruit shop activity is related to developing knowledge and understanding of the world.

LESSON 2

OBJECTIVES
● To develop sorting skills by touching and feeling.
● To develop an idea of texture.

RESOURCES

Main teaching activity: A range of fruits with interesting textures, including an orange, apple, plum, pineapple, kiwi fruit and strawberry.
Group activities: 1. Sorting rings and labels. **2.** A cutting board, knife and bowl; photocopiable page 36. **3.** The 'fruit shop' role-play area from Lesson 1.
Plenary: Photocopiable page 37.

Vocabulary

smooth, rough, prickly, sharp, squashy, hard, soft, sticky, juicy, wet

PREPARATION

Write some of the set labels, using words that you want to introduce during the Group activities. Make a copy of photocopiable page 36 and an enlarged (A3) copy of page 37.

INTRODUCTION

Sit the children in a circle so that they can see the fruit. Talk for a few minutes about the names of the fruits they can see.

MAIN TEACHING ACTIVITY

Pass the apple around. Ask the children to touch it and think about how it feels. If they are able to, let them tell you what it feels like; otherwise, talk about its texture being hard and smooth as it is passed around the group. Next, pass the pineapple around and invite the children to comment on this fruit. They may say that it is heavy, prickly, hard and rough. Accept all responses, asking the children each time to say why they think that. The purpose is to find out what the children already know. Continue to pass around different types of fruit and talk about the textures until you are confident that the children understand what 'texture' means.

GROUP ACTIVITIES

1. Gather six to eight children around the sorting rings and fruit. Allow them to handle the fruit and talk about what they can feel. Ask them to put all the fruit that is smooth into one sorting ring and all the fruit that is not smooth into another. Label the rings 'smooth' and 'not smooth'. Sort the fruit again, using different criteria. Reinforce the learning objective: using the sense of touch to sort fruit.
2. Ask an adult helper to make a fruit salad with groups of up to six children. Brief the adult to talk about the juice and the 'squashiness' of the fruit. Give him or her a copy of page 36: a list of prompt words to use with the children, describing what the fruit feels like.
3. Allow a group of children to play in the 'fruit shop' role-play area.

DIFFERENTIATION

With the more able or older children, when the fruits have been sorted, talk about how they are similar and how they are different. They may want to talk about how the fruits look as well as how they feel – for example: *Does the pineapple look prickly? Why?*

The younger or less able children need to be introduced to the language a word at a time. Ask an adult helper to pass around all the smooth fruit for the children to feel to help them understand what you mean by 'smooth'. Afterwards, pass the pineapple around and describe the texture to them while they handle the fruit. Repeat this with other fruits in your collection.

ASSESSMENT

Note which children already have the vocabulary to describe texture at the beginning of the activity, so that you can extend this. Set up a display of objects in the classroom with different textures for the children to explore, and note those who can sort using their sense of touch.

PLENARY

Talk about the fruit salad the children have made. *Are the textures different now the fruit has been cut up? Why isn't the pineapple prickly any more?* This will lead to a discussion about the differences between the way that fruit feels on the inside and on the outside. Complete page 37 with the children.

OUTCOMES

● Can find out about fruit by touching and feeling.
● Can compare fruit before and after peeling, noting similarities and differences.

LINKS

Between units: there are links to the activities in Unit 4, where the children are asked to explore a variety of materials using their senses.

LESSON 3

Objective	● To develop sorting skills by using the sense of smell.
Resources	A collection of fruits including an orange, a banana, an apple and a strawberry (other fruits with a distinctive and easily recognisable scent will do), each chopped up into a disposable cup with a paper cover held on with an elastic band.
Main activity	Talk to the children about how we smell things. Make sure they understand that we use our noses to smell. Emphasise the importance of not smelling things we are unfamiliar with: it might be dangerous. It is safe to do so in this lesson, because they will only be smelling familiar fruit to try and guess what is in each pot. 　　One at a time, pass the cups around the class and ask the children to guess what fruit is in each cup. Invite those who can to describe the smell, using words such as 'sweet' and 'tangy'. They could also use words and phrases related to the names of fruits, such as 'orangey' or 'like a pineapple'. (This is difficult for very young children, however, and is not essential.) As each cup returns to you, remove the paper cover and pass the cup around again so that the children can see whether they were right. 　　Set up a similar Group activity, using different fruits, for some of the children to play during the day.
Differentiation	Less able children, and those who are still unfamiliar with the names of the fruits, may need to repeat the activity in smaller groups with an adult. Ask more able children to make their own pots (under supervision), containing different fruits for their friends to guess.
Assessment	Invite the children to record by drawing the fruits that they think are in each pot. Keep these drawings as evidence of the children's ability to use their sense of smell to identify fruit.
Plenary	Share the fruit salad and talk about the different smells of the fruits. Remind the children of the names of the different fruits.
Outcomes	● Can link the sense of smell to the nose. ● Can identify fruit by using the sense of smell.

LESSON 4

Objective	● To develop sorting skills by using the sense of taste.
Resources	A selection of fruits that have different tastes (ones that you know the children like), each cut up and placed in a sealed container. Be aware of any fruit allergies or dietary restrictions.
Main activity	Talk to the children about how we taste things. Make sure they understand that we taste using the tongue and mouth. Emphasise the dangers of eating things that we are not used to, and tell them that they should only play the following game with a trusted adult. Explain that they are going to guess what fruit they are eating without seeing it. Ask one child to close his or her eyes, then place a piece of fruit onto the child's tongue and invite him or her to eat it. Ask questions such as: *Is the fruit crunchy or soft? Is it dry or juicy? Is it sweet or sour?* Finally, ask the child whether he or she can identify the fruit using the sense of taste alone. Repeat the activity with other children, until they have all had a turn.
Differentiation	Give less able children a piece of orange each and invite them to say what the fruit tastes like. Encourage the use of vocabulary as suggested above. Repeat this activity with several different kinds of familiar fruit before letting the children play the game (as above) with an adult helper. Challenge the more able group with more exotic fruits that they will not easily recognise straight away. You may wish to introduce the children to these more unusual tastes before playing.
Assessment	Ask the children to draw the fruit they think they are tasting. Keep their drawings as a record.
Plenary	Share the fruit salad at snack time, encouraging the children to describe the different tastes.
Outcomes	● Can use the sense of taste to find out about fruit. ● Can link the sense of taste to the tongue and mouth.

LESSON 5

OBJECTIVES
● To know that we need to drink to stay alive.
● To develop recording skills through sorting.

RESOURCES
Main teaching activity: Fruit juices of different varieties (including orange, apple, pineapple, blackcurrant, strawberry and grapefruit), containing no (or few) additives and no added sugar; jugs, disposable cups.
Group activities: 1. Name cards for the children; a sheet of paper for each fruit drink with a picture of the fruit in each corner (include a sheet for water). **2.** Paper, coloured pencils or crayons, sugar paper, adhesive. **3.** Jugs, tap water.

Vocabulary
fruity, flavour, juice, favourite, best, thirsty, alive

PREPARATION
Check for any fruit allergies or dietary restrictions. Pour small quantities of the fruit juices into jugs; include a jug of water.

INTRODUCTION
Show the children the different fruit drinks and the water. Explain that we all need to drink if we are to stay alive. Ask the children whether they are thirsty. Explain that when they feel thirsty, their body is telling them that they need a drink.

MAIN TEACHING ACTIVITY
Ask the children what drinks they like best. *Do you like water?* Make a list on the board or flip chart of all the fruit drinks the children like, using the names and sketches of the fruits. If different children choose the same drink, tally their responses alongside the fruit. Next, invite the children to choose and enjoy a small drink from the collection. Encourage them to try one that they are unfamiliar with, and to drink the water on its own also.

GROUP ACTIVITIES
1. Work with a group of eight to ten children. Ask them which drink they like best of the ones on offer. Display the sheets with pictures of the fruits on a table along with the name cards. Ask the children to point to the picture of the fruit from which their favourite drink is made (or to

the water, if this is preferred). Challenge each child to take his or her name card from the group and place it on the sheet of paper representing his or her choice. Count and record how many name cards there are on each sheet of paper. Which drink did the group like best?

2. Ask an adult helper to talk to the children about all the kinds of drinks that need to have water added. The children should draw pictures of all the drinks they have thought of and stick them to a sheet of sugar paper: tea, coffee, squashes, powdered fizzy drinks and so on.

3. Organise small groups of children to fill jugs with water for snack time each day.

DIFFERENTIATION

Allow less able children to express their choice of a favourite drink. Emphasise the importance of drinking for staying alive.

Talk to the more able group about the range of drinks in your collection. Which drink does each child like best? Ask them to draw a picture of the fruit from which their favourite drink is made. When you have all the pictures from this group, arrange them into columns to make a pictogram. Count and record how many pictures are in each column, then transfer this data to a block graph (using a computer if possible).

ASSESSMENT

Listen to the children's conversations as they talk about their favourite drinks. Question them to see whether they understand that when they feel thirst, they need a drink.

PLENARY

Talk to the children about the fruit juices they have been drinking. Talk about the number of children who chose to drink water. Explain that it is very important to drink water at regular intervals, and not just fruit juices and other sugary drinks. Explain why: too much sugar is bad for your teeth, and sugary drinks can make you more instead of less thirsty. Encourage them to drink a cup of water at this point, and reinforce the learning objective throughout the day by inviting them to drink water at regular intervals.

OUTCOMES

● Know that they need to drink to stay alive.
● Know that thirst is the body's way of saying 'Give me a drink'.
● (More able children) Can begin to organise information in graphical form.

LINKS

Between units: this lesson is linked to Unit 2, Lesson 4 on caring for pets.
Across the curriculum: the children recognising their own name links to communication, language and literacy.

LESSON 6

OBJECTIVE
● To learn that not all things are safe to touch, smell and taste.

RESOURCES

Main teaching activity: Stickers from photocopiable page 38, adhesive; a collection of empty, washed containers of household cleaners, some of which have a range of signs on the packaging showing that we should not touch, taste or smell them. Include washing powder, dishwasher powder and tablets, polish, disinfectant and other cleaners that have a black cross on an orange background. Also include some items (such as spray polish and washing-up liquid) that do not have the cross, but nevertheless should only be used under supervision.

Group activities: 1. Photocopiable page 38, scissors, adhesive. **2.** Pictures of household items (cut from magazines) that are and that are not safe to touch (see above – also shampoo, soap, bubble bath, food); two sheets of paper, glue sticks. **3.** Photocopiable page 39, pencils.

Vocabulary

safe, not safe, dangerous, poison, poisonous, hazard, acid, disinfectant, cleaner

PREPARATION

Wash out all of the empty containers, and cut out magazine pictures for Group activity 2. You may wish to make these a permanent resource by mounting them onto cardboard and laminating them. Make copies of the 'Do not touch' stickers on photocopiable page 39. Send a letter to parents and carers to let them know you will be doing this lesson, so that they can reinforce the learning objective at home to give the children a consistent message.

INTRODUCTION

Show the children the collection of containers. *Do you recognise any of these? Do you have some of these in your cupboard at home?*

MAIN TEACHING ACTIVITY

Select the washing powder container and point out the sign on the side. Can any of the children tell you what this sign means? *It means that the contents of the container are dangerous and that we should never touch, smell or (worst of all) taste the contents.* Explain the possible consequences of doing so (be sensitive to the children's feelings). Explain that the sign showing a black cross on an orange square means 'poisonous'. Stick the 'Do not touch' label from page 38 onto the container. Repeat this activity with the other containers and photocopied labels.

GROUP ACTIVITIES

1. Work with groups of six children to talk about the materials that were originally in the containers you have collected. Invite them to find the label on each container that tells them not to touch, smell or taste the contents. Give each child a copy of page 38, and together add 'Do not touch' labels to the materials that are dangerous.

2. Ask an adult helper to reinforce the message by talking to groups of up to four children about the pictures you have cut from magazines. Ask the children to place the materials that are safe to touch on one sheet of paper, and those that are not on another. Compare the numbers of pictures on each sheet of paper. Now ask the children whether any of the materials are safe to smell or taste. Do they decide that there are no pictures of things that are safe to smell or taste? Reinforce the message that it is **never** safe to smell or taste anything unless an adult they know has said that it is safe to do so.

3. Give the children a copy of photocopiable page 39 and ask them to circle the sign on each picture that shows they should never touch the object.

DIFFERENTIATION

You may wish to consider with the more able children other things that are not safe to touch, smell or taste, such as wild berries, alcohol, cigarettes and medicines.

Repeat Group activity 3 with less able children. Work with individuals or pairs to circle the signs on the pictures, relating them to the actual bottles in your collection if possible.

ASSESSMENT

It is important that the children learn that not all things are safe for them to touch, smell and (particularly) taste, and these issues must be handled sensitively. Note those children who do not yet understand the consequences of touching things without thinking first, and continue to reinforce this message in other activities.

PLENARY

Talk to the children again about the cleaning materials in your collection and how it is not safe to touch, smell or taste any of them. Explain that they are intended to kill germs, which means that they are poisonous and so can be harmful to people. Allow the children to talk freely about the tasks and what they have learned.

OUTCOME

● Begin to learn how to keep themselves safe by knowing that not all things are safe to touch, smell and taste.

LINKS

Between units: the same learning objective is repeated in other contexts in lessons in Units 2, 3, 4, 5 and 8.

Context: 'FEELY BAG' ACTIVITIES

The next four lessons are about the senses, and are taught through activities involving the use of 'feely bags'. Make sure that you do not include items with sharp edges. Very young children enjoy these games, and they can be set up in the classroom as interactive displays for children to access throughout the weeks that follow.

LESSON 7

Objective	● To learn which parts of the body are used to smell, touch, see, hear and taste.
Resources	The song 'I've got a body' from *Spring Tinderbox* (A&C Black); large pictures of a tongue, ear, eye, nose and hand; card labels, paints and crayons in a range of colours; paper, adhesive sticks; a computer, the program *My World* from Semerc (optional).
Main activity	Teach the children the song 'I've got a body', adding verses about taste, touch, seeing and hearing. Ask the children to draw or paint pictures of their favourite flavours (for example, ice cream or pizza). Stick these onto a previously painted picture of a large tongue. Repeat the task with sounds we like to hear, favourite colours, favourite smells and things we like to touch: stick the children's pictures onto large paintings of an ear, an eye, a nose and a hand respectively. 　Ask the children to write labels for the parts of the body that we use to see, hear, smell, touch and taste. They can draw a body and attach the labels. Alternatively, this could be done on a computer using *My World* if you wish. 　Working with groups of six children, give each child an outline of a face. Ask them: *Draw what we see with.* Now ask them to draw what we hear with, and so on.
Differentiation	Talk with more able children about other parts of the body we can feel with. *Can you feel anything with your feet? How do you know?* Play additional games with less able children to develop their skills in exploring with the senses.
Assessment	In the group work, note which children draw the features in the correct order (starting with the eyes), which children copy from others and so on.
Plenary	Reinforce the safety issues relating to touches, smells and tastes. Talk about the dangers to ears and eyes of loud noise and looking at the Sun.
Outcomes	● Know which parts of the body we use to hear, see, smell and taste, and which main parts we use to feel and touch. ● Have begun to think about how to look after our bodies and protect our hearing and sight.

LESSON 8

OBJECTIVES
● To learn that we can use our fingers and hands to touch and feel, and that we can use this sense to identify objects.
● To explore and describe a range of objects that have different shapes and textures.

RESOURCES
Main teaching activity: Several feely bags, each containing a familiar object that has an interesting and distinctive surface for feeling (a ball of cotton wool, ceramic teapot, cup, toothbrush, hairbrush, metal spoon, sticklebrick, tennis ball, teddy bear, metal saucepan, wooden spoon and handkerchief); an ice cube and a rubber ball.
Group activities: 1. As for Main teaching activity. **2.** Paper, pencils. **3.** Collections of similar objects for printing (such as cotton reels, toy car wheels, cotton wool balls, train track pieces, Lego bricks), thickly mixed paint in a range of colours, polystyrene trays, sponges, paper, aprons.

Vocabulary
hard, soft, fluffy, smooth, rough, bumpy, bendy, squashy

PREPARATION
Mix paint in a range of colours to a fairly thick consistency for printing.

INTRODUCTION
Pass an ice cube around the group of children and ask them to say what it feels like. Encourage them to use words such as 'slippery', 'cold', 'hard', 'smooth' and 'icy'. Shrieks may also be included! Ask them whether it is easy to hold the ice cube, whether it fits inside their hand and whether it has a recognisable shape. The answers may change as the activity goes on. Repeat this activity with a rubber ball or similar object.

MAIN TEACHING ACTIVITY

Explain to the children that you have several bags, with an object hidden inside each one. Say that you are going to play a game together: you are going to ask someone to guess what the object inside the bag is just by using the sense of touch, without looking. Pass the bag to a child who you know will be able to say a little about the object in the bag. Ask him or her to say something about the object. *Do you know what the object is? How do you know? Does it have a special shape that helps you to say what it is? Does the object fit inside your hand? Does it have a handle? How does it feel? Is it smooth or rough? Hard or soft?* Continue with another object and a different child, until a few children have had a turn at guessing an object.

GROUP ACTIVITIES

1. Repeat the Main teaching activity with a group of six children, giving all the children an opportunity to guess a new object inside each bag.
2. Allow one group to play the game independently by giving them a bag containing several different objects for them to guess. Ask them to draw pictures of all the objects they think are inside the bag. At the end of the activity, remove the objects to see whether they have guessed them all correctly. Use an additional adult helper for this if possible.
3. Organise a group to try printing with a range of objects (see Resources).

DIFFERENTIATION

With the less able children, pass a teapot around the group, pointing out the different parts that they can feel. Ask them whether they can feel the shape of the teapot's handle and spout. *Can you hold the teapot in your hand?* Now place the teapot inside a bag and ask the children to feel the things you have talked about.

More able children can move quickly to the independent group task. Afterwards, ask them to make a game for their friends: putting several objects inside a bag and challenging their friends to identify them by touch. Ask them why they chose the objects they did.

ASSESSMENT

Observe the children as they feel the object in the bag. Are they thinking about the shape and texture? Note those children who understand easily, and move them on to the extension task (making a game). Continue to focus on the children who are not yet able to describe the object in terms of their sense of touch, even though they may be able to identify it.

PLENARY

Look at the prints together. Ask the children whether they can guess which object has made each print from its shape and texture. Make a display of the prints and objects for the children to match during the week.

OUTCOMES

- Can identify objects by feeling their shape and texture.
- Can describe similarities and differences between objects.
- Can talk about the materials from which different objects are made.

LINKS

Between units: this lesson can be taught within the set of lessons in Unit 4 based on the 'hardware store' role-play area, which develops the vocabulary of materials and their properties.
Across the curriculum: identifying an object from one face of its shape begins to develop the children's geography skills.

LESSON 9

OBJECTIVE
● To learn to identify objects from the sounds they make.

RESOURCES

Main teaching activity: Feely bags containing a bell, a doorbell, a baby's rattle, a container (with a tight-fitting lid) full of water, a full packet of crisps, a drum, a beater and other easily recognisable musical instruments.
Group activities: 1. A cassette with a number of sounds made by different objects recorded on it; a cassette player. It is easy to make your own tape, but several commercial sound matching games are available. **2.** A sound story book, a computer. Talking books for use on a computer are produced by Sherston Software and by Oxford University Press (to support their Oxford Reading Tree scheme). You can pick up a variety of books from bookshops that have high-quality sound effects. **3.** Shopping catalogues, scissors. **4.** A selection of percussion instruments, strikers and scrapers.
Plenary: *A Good Night's Sleep* by Martin Waddell (Walker Books) or *We're Going on a Bear Hunt* by Michael Rosen (Walker Books).

Vocabulary
tinkle, swish, crackle, rattle, high, low, loud, quiet, soft

PREPARATION

Put the objects inside separate bags and put them where you intend to do the Main teaching activity well before the lesson. This will ensure that the children do not hear any of the objects being moved before the activity begins.

INTRODUCTION

Put your hand inside a bag and find a bell. Ring the bell while it is still inside the bag, and ask the children to say what is making the sound. Do they find this easy?

MAIN TEACHING ACTIVITY

Explain that you have other objects inside the bags that make different sounds. Invite the children to guess what is making the sound as you move each object inside its bag. Talk about the kind of sound each object makes. *Is it loud or quiet?* Say that another word for 'quiet' is 'soft'. *Does the object crackle or splash? Is it a high sound or a low sound? Does any sound remind you of what the object is used for? For example, why does a bell make a loud noise?*

GROUP ACTIVITIES

1. Ask an adult helper to play a tape of sounds to a group of four children. Can they guess what objects are making the sounds? Reinforce the idea that the children are using their ears to listen carefully and identify what is making the sound.
2. Ask another adult helper to share a sound book (see Resources) with pairs of children.
3. Work with a group of six to eight children, cutting pictures of items that make sounds (such as an alarm clock, a drill, a car, a microwave oven, a cuckoo clock) from shopping catalogues and talking about the sounds these items make.

4. Give the children a small selection of percussion instruments, strikers and scrapers; let them investigate the different sounds that can be made with these.

DIFFERENTIATION

For less able children, ask an adult or older child pair up and help in the sound matching game. Give the adults clear guidance before the task to help them ensure that the children are learning the vocabulary associated with sound.

Give the more able group a bag containing several different percussion instruments. Ask them to take turns to make a sound while the rest of the group guess what the instrument is.

ASSESSMENT

During the Main teaching activity, invite the children to record what they think is making each sound in the bags (or ask an adult helper to record their comments). Use this record to plan additional play activities (if necessary) to reinforce the learning objective.

PLENARY

Read out the story of *A Good Night's Sleep* or *We're Going on a Bear Hunt* (see Resources). Invite the children to join in with the sound effects, using body percussion and the instruments from Group activity 4.

OUTCOMES

● Know that they use their ears to hear.
● Can recognise familiar objects from the sounds they make.

LINKS

Across the curriculum: give the children opportunities to add sound effects to a poem or song in creative development activities. Also give them a range of percussion instruments and invite them to create a musical composition of loud, soft, high and low sounds. Link the lesson to literacy by asking them to join in reading either of the books used in the Plenary session.

LESSON 10

OBJECTIVE

● To begin to use their senses to identify similarities and differences.

RESOURCES

Main teaching activity: Domino cards with matching textures, pictures and colours (these are available from good educational equipment catalogues); matching sound pots (see Preparation).
Group activities: 1 and 2. An additional selection of the resources used in the Main teaching activity.

Vocabulary

similar, same, different, scratchy, tinkly, high, low, rattle, loud, quiet. Also vocabulary from Lesson 8.

PREPARATION

Make a set of pairs of sound pots from disposable cups and a range of materials, including small bells, rice, dried peas, nails and sand. Make a set of domino cards containing a mixture of textures, colours and pictures: divide each rectangular card shape into two and stick a textured material on one half and a colour or picture on the other. Continue until you have a set that will allow you to complete a circuit by matching the ends.

INTRODUCTION

Introduce the sound pots to the children. Shake two of the pots, making sure that they do not have the same sound. Ask the children to say whether the sounds are the same or different. *Why are the sounds different? Is one sound louder than the other one? Does it make a different kind of sound? Is it more tinkly? Can any of you guess what is making this sound?*

MAIN TEACHING ACTIVITY

Shake two more pots and ask the children about these sounds. Use questions (as above) to make them think about how the sounds are the same and how they are different. Next, introduce the domino cards to the children. Invite a child to feel one of the textures (with his or her eyes closed if this will help). *What does the material feel like? Can you find a card that has the same texture?* Place this card at the end of the first domino. Talk about the pictures or colours at the other ends of the cards. Can the children find matching colours or pictures by looking? Invite them to say why they chose the card they did. You should now have a texture at each end of the row of dominoes. Invite the children to find a matching texture to place at each end, and to say why they chose the cards they did. *How are the two textures the same or different?*

GROUP ACTIVITIES

1. Play the matching domino game with a group of six to eight children, either all together (as above) or by distributing the cards to give each child a more limited choice. Carry on until the set is complete.

2. Allow one group to play with the sound pots, trying to match them up.

DIFFERENTIATION

Ask more able children to make their own sound pots matching game for their friends to play.

Work with less able children, using commercial domino sets to focus on matching textures or pictures separately. Talk to the children about how the pictures are different and how they are the same.

ASSESSMENT

Make a note of those children who are confident about using their senses to explore the sounds, textures and pictures, and those who have the vocabulary they need to explain their choices.

PLENARY

Play the dominoes game at the end of the session, if most of the children are able to match up the various features of the dominoes. Otherwise, play the matching game with the sound pots.

OUTCOME

● Can begin to use more than one sense to explore a range of objects and to identify similarities and differences.

LINKS

Between units: this lesson links to the work on materials in Unit 4.

ASSESSMENT

LESSON 11

OBJECTIVES

● To assess the children's ability to explore using all five senses and to identify familiar objects.
● To reinforce the use of drawing to record findings in an investigation.

RESOURCES

Assessment activities: 1. Several boxes of different sizes; a familiar object for each box, including two teapots, a cup, a bell, an orange, a teabag, a teddy bear; wrapping paper, tissue paper, adhesive tape; a further set of boxes with familiar objects to be used for ongoing assessment. **2.** Food samples for the children to taste and identify, including cheese, chocolate, apple, tomato, cucumber and orange.

PREPARATION

Place an object inside each box and wrap the box with wrapping paper. Make sure that the smells of the orange and teabag come through by punching a few holes in each box. Provide a hole in the side of one box large enough for the children to feel the teddy bear. Wrap the cup and one of the teapots directly in tissue paper so that their shapes can easily be seen.

Check for any food allergies or dietary restrictions when selecting the food samples. Cut the food items into bite-sized pieces, place them on a plate and cover them.

INTRODUCTION

Work with groups of four children. Show them the teapot wrapped in tissue paper, and ask them what they think is wrapped inside the parcel. *How do you know?* Note whether they recognise the handle and spout. Sing the rhyme 'I'm a little teapot' (from *This Little Puffin* compiled by Elizabeth Matterson, Penguin Books) to reinforce the features of a teapot. Place the second, unwrapped teapot alongside the first one to show that the shapes are the same or similar. Talk about this if necessary.

ASSESSMENT ACTIVITY 1

Allow the children to play with the other parcels. Observe closely to see which children use their senses to try to discover what is inside each parcel. Listen to their conversations and talk to them about what they can feel, smell, hear and see. Do they have the vocabulary to describe the texture and shape that helps them to identify the teddy bear? Can they use their sense of smell to identify the orange? How many children can recognise the bell by using their sense of hearing? After about five minutes, ask the children to talk about what they think is inside the parcels. Does anyone disagree?

Further assessment opportunities
Leave a set of wrapped parcels on the side for the children to interact with during the week. This will allow you to note which children are able to develop their exploration skills, and to assess whether you need to organise additional activities to reinforce the learning.

ASSESSMENT ACTIVITY 2

With a group of four children, explain that you are going to explore the tastes of some food items. They should try to guess what the food items are, but keep their guesses secret until all the children have had a chance to taste the items. Ask the children to close their eyes, and place a piece of apple on each child's tongue. Now say *Open your eyes*, and ask the children to draw a picture of what they think the food item was. Make sure that they have no opportunity to copy each other. Repeat the process for all the food items. At the end of the activity, talk about the children's pictures. Tell them that you want to keep their 'recordings' because the pictures show how well they have investigated the different tastes.

Assessment outcomes
Most of the children should be able to explore a range of familiar objects using their senses. Note which children need additional practice.

Context: THE BABY CLINIC OR HEALTH CENTRE

The next five lessons are set in the context of a 'Baby clinic'. Set up a baby clinic in the role-play area, to include dolls, other toys and baby clothes. Make sure that there is a display space close to this area for the children's photographs and pictures.

LESSON 12

OBJECTIVE
● To recognise and learn the names of parts of the body and be able to say what they are used for.

RESOURCES

Main teaching activity: The songs 'I've got a body' from *Tinderbox* (A&C Black) and 'I have two ears' by Gill Daniell from *Count Me In* (A&C Black).
Group activities: 1. Pictures of people cut from magazines, adhesive sticks, card, scissors.
2. People jigsaws from a commercial source.
3. Photocopiable page 40 and/or a computer with a copy of *My World*. **4.** Paper and paints in a range of colours, card labels. Post-it notes and felt-tipped pens for the extension activity.

Vocabulary

head, hands, fingers, arm, leg, foot, feet, toes, eyes, mouth, nose, ears, lips, tongue, neck, back, bottom, stomach

PREPARATION

Set up the painting activity for the children to access. Brief adult helpers about the intended learning outcome of the Group activity they are supporting.

INTRODUCTION

Teach the children the song 'I've got a body' from *Tinderbox*. Make up additional verses for stamping, walking, clapping, clicking (fingers) and nodding.

MAIN TEACHING ACTIVITY

Ask the children which part of the body they use to clap, stamp, walk and so on. Use the song 'I have two ears' to reinforce these ideas (or repeat 'I've got a body'). Now ask them to point to another part of the body. Can they say what it is called, how many of it they have, and what they can do with it/them? Sing this as another verse. Continue with this until the children cannot think of any more body parts or become restless.

GROUP ACTIVITIES

1. Organise a group of four children to make people jigsaws by cutting pictures of people from magazines, mounting them on card and cutting off the arms and legs ready to reassemble. Talk about what they use each part of the body for.
2. Allow one group of children to work on people jigsaws from a commercial source.
3. Adult helpers can work with pairs of children to label body parts on a computer, using *My World*, and/or work with small groups to complete photocopiable page 40.
4. Ask the children to paint pictures of themselves. Display the finished paintings with labels attached to the relevant parts of the body.

DIFFERENTIATION

Allow more able children to continue as far as they can with the labelling activity. They could work with an adult, using Post-it notes and a live model to label as many body parts as they can. Encourage them to use words such as: 'elbow', 'waist', 'knee', 'shoulder', 'chest', 'wrist', 'nostril', 'chin', 'cheek', 'eyebrow', 'forehead', 'knuckle', 'hips', 'thigh', 'ankle', 'heel'.
    Play a 'Point to the body part' game with less able children: name different body parts and ask the children to point to each in turn. Take them as far as you can. The song 'Put your finger on your head' by Wendy Guthrie in *Okki-tokki-unga* (A&C Black) is useful for this; you can add new verses to teach the names of different parts.

ASSESSMENT

Note those children who are able to name most of the external parts of the body, and are attaining Level 1 in this aspect of science. Note those children who can recognise and point to different body parts and features, attaining the relevant Early Learning Goal.

PLENARY

Sing a variety of songs and number rhymes about the body, using appropriate actions to accompany the words.

OUTCOMES

● Can identify some external parts of the human body and recognise their names.
● Can talk about what they are doing.

LINKS

Between units: this lesson links with those in Unit 2 on the body parts of animals.
Across the curriculum: the learning in this lesson can be reinforced through physical development activities that involve using hands, fingers, arms, legs, feet and toes. The parts of the body can be used as a context in which to develop counting activities.

LESSON 13

Objective	● To learn that we use different parts of our bodies to move in different ways.
Resources	A large space for the children to move in; balancing apparatus, mats, benches, low tables, skipping ropes, stilts, hoops, stepping-stones; paper, coloured pencils or crayons. Specialist PE equipment may be necessary to meet the needs of individual children.

Main activity	Do your established warm-up activity for physical development activities. Tell the children that they are going to move in lots of different ways, using different parts of their body. Invite them to move using their feet and legs: encourage and develop skipping, creeping, hopping, walking, jumping and running movements. Develop the theme by getting the children to move in different directions and to use hands as well as feet.
	   Move on to a range of apparatus including balance beams, low tables, mats and benches. Give the children a range of small equipment including skipping ropes, hoops, stilts and stepping-stones. Invite them to use the equipment to move in different ways, using different parts of their body.
	   Ask the children to record all the different ways they can move by drawing pictures. Use their pictures to make a wall frieze of children on the move.

Differentiation	Less able children could use one type of equipment or one piece of apparatus at a time and develop their activities over a series of six lessons. Talk about one kind of movement during each lesson to focus learning and make the objective more specific (for example, balancing in week 1, skipping in week 2, jumping in week 3). For more able children, make the apparatus more challenging. You could develop an obstacle course for them to use, adding and changing items in each lesson to encourage them to use different parts of the body and to move in different ways. For example, the course could be constructed to develop balancing one day and crawling, jumping and climbing the next; or using a horizontal ladder (or plank) one day and using a sloping ladder the next.
Assessment	Note those children who can distinguish a number of different ways of moving, and who are beginning to use different body parts to improve the quality of their movements (for example, outstretched arms for balancing).
Plenary	Talk about all the ways that the children moved as you add their pictures to your frieze. Finish by singing one of your favourite movement songs.
Outcome	● Know that we can move in many different ways, using different parts of our bodies and sometimes more than one part at a time.

LESSON 14

OBJECTIVE
● To know that we all grow and change as we get older.

RESOURCES
Main teaching activity: A picture of yourself as a baby and at present; if possible, items of clothing and toys that belonged to you and the children as a small child; a video of a baby and toddler (if available).
Group activities: 1. Pictures of the children as babies and at the present time, A3 paper, speech bubbles cut from white paper, adhesive, a felt-tipped pen, a display board. **2.** A collection of baby clothes and toys. **3.** A collection of girls' and boys' clothing, photocopiable page 41, pencils. **4.** Several baskets.

PREPARATION
Take photographs of all the children, either using a digital camera or in time to have the film developed before the lesson. Send a letter home asking parents and carers for photographs of the children when they were babies, and for some of their baby clothes and toys.

INTRODUCTION
Look at the collection of baby clothes, toys and photographs with the children. Give them some time to handle the items carefully. Talk about the toys. *Does anyone have a younger brother or sister at home who has the same toys?* Ask the children who they think wears the clothes. Would they fit them still, or have they grown too much?

MAIN TEACHING ACTIVITY
Show the children a photograph of yourself (or another teacher or child) as a baby. Ask them how the person in the photo looks. *Are they sitting, lying or standing? How big are they? Do they have hair, teeth?* Now show them a photo of yourself now. *Look at the same person now. Has anything changed about that person? What has changed?* Make a list of all the things that have changed: the differences between the two pictures.

Show the children a video of a baby and a toddler, and ask them to say how the movements have changed. Talk about how the toddler moves. *Are we safer on our feet now? Why is this?* Explain that we gain a better balance as we get older.

Vocabulary

change, different, small, smaller, tiny, bigger, taller, fatter, same

GROUP ACTIVITIES

1. Work with groups of four children. Talk about how they look in their baby photographs and how they look now, using the photographs they have brought from home and those taken recently in school. The children can write how they have changed in the speech bubbles, or you can scribe for them. Fold a sheet of A3 paper in half and add the titles 'Me as a baby' and 'Me now'. Stick the photographs on either side of the sheet and add the speech bubbles in the appropriate places. Fix the sheet to the display board with 'Look how I've changed!' in huge letters at the top. Repeat the activity until all the children have done it.

2. Ask an adult helper to talk to groups of six children about the collections of baby clothes and toys. They should talk about the size and style of the clothes, and encourage the children to identify fabrics and fastenings. Would the clothes fit them? Why not? Who would wear them? Can they name the toys? Can they say how the baby plays with them?

3. Give the children matching sets of baby and children's clothes to sort into pairs. Ask them to match the items on photocopiable page 41 (for example, the baby dungarees match to the trousers).

4. Allow a group of four children to play in the role-play area, sorting the baby clothes into items of the same type (socks, pullovers and so on) in different baskets.

DIFFERENTIATION

With less able children, make a collection of baby things (such as a rattle, bottle, tin of baby food, bath, changing mat, nappy, clothes and car seat). Talk about how these are used by parents or the baby. Make up a separate display.

Give more able children a set of photographs of people at different stages in their life and ask them to put these in order. Can they say how the people have changed?

ASSESSMENT

Note those children who understand that we change as we get older through growing, playing and doing more complicated things. This will give you assessment information to use in planning the next lesson, which might include looking at finer differences between age groups (such as wrinkles and grey hair).

PLENARY

Make a display of all the baby things collected for this lesson, talking about the differences and reinforcing the children's awareness that we all change as we grow.

OUTCOMES

● Can sort and match items of clothing of very different sizes and explain how they would have fitted everyone at a certain stage in their life.
● Know that we all change as we grow older.

LINKS

Between units: this lesson links to the lessons in Unit 2 on animal growth.
Across the curriculum: the children can read the story *Once There Were Giants* by Martin Waddell (Walker Books) as part of a literacy activity. They can sort items of clothing into pairs as part of a numeracy lesson.

LESSON 15

Objective	● To learn that we can all do many things for ourselves.
Resources	An adult accompanied by a baby; things for the baby (a baby bath, a change of clothes, warm water, a towel, feeding implements); a warm draught-free place; paper, pencils, paints; a large picture of a baby.

Main activity	Introduce the adult and baby. Give the children time to ask questions and talk about the baby. Invite the adult to bath, dress and feed the baby if possible. Talk to the children about what is happening, and point out all the things that the adult has to do for the baby because the baby is unable to do these things for him- or herself. Invite the children to ask questions about what the baby is and is not able to do.
	   Talk to the children about whether they are now able to do some of these things for themselves. Make a list of the things they can now do, and invite them to record what they have discovered by drawing pictures and placing them alongside the correct words in the list. Add to the list during the week as you note more things that the children can do for themselves.
	   Ask the children to draw a speech bubble and write in it what they can do now that they have grown up. Ask them whether these are things that they could do as a baby.
	   Ask the children to paint pictures of their own faces. Let them dry and then cut them out to include in a display.

Differentiation	Ask more able children to extend the list beyond what you have recorded together by writing a long list of all the things that they can do now. Act as a scribe for less able children as they produce a similar list, and work with groups of four to question them and relate their ideas back to what they saw when the baby was bathed.
Assessment	Watch the children during the Main activity and note those who ask questions. Listen to what they ask: does the question have an obvious answer?
Plenary	Stick a picture of a baby to the centre of a display board, and invite the children to contribute to a speech bubble saying what the baby is able to do by him- or herself. Add the children's faces and their speech bubbles, reading them out loud as you do so.
Outcomes	● Know what babies are and are not able to do for themselves. ● Understand that as young children get older, they are able to do more things for themselves.

LESSON 16

OBJECTIVE

● To investigate similarities and differences between us.

RESOURCES

Group activities: 1. Paint and crayons in a range of colours including skin tones; paper, paint brushes; a large wall area for display. **2.** Photocopiable page 42, pencils. **4.** A range of collage materials including disposable plates, eye-coloured circles, hair-coloured wool, scissors, PVA glue. **5.** Paint, polystyrene trays, a bowl, a sponge, water, soap, a towel.

Vocabulary
freckles, hair, long, short, fair, blonde, dark, brown, green, blue, fat, thin, spectacles, tall, short, similar, similarities, different, differences

PREPARATION

Mix skin tone paints and other colours if your children are not yet mixing their own colours. Cut some of the wool into different (life-sized) lengths for hair.

INTRODUCTION

Tell the children that you are going to make a display together to show all the things that are the same about them, and all the things that are different. Ask two children who have some similar features and some contrasting features to act as models for the Main teaching activity.

MAIN TEACHING ACTIVITY

Ask the two 'models' to stand at the front of the class. Ask the other children to look very carefully at one of them. What can they tell you about the colour of this child's hair and eyes, how tall the child is, how long the child's hair is and so on? Repeat the task with the second child. Now ask the class to look carefully at both of the children. *Can you see anything about them that is the same? For example, do they have the same colour hair or eyes? Can you see any differences between them?*

GROUP ACTIVITIES

1. Ask an adult helper to work with groups of four children as they paint pictures of themselves. The children should pay particular attention to the colour of their eyes, skin and hair, and be sure to paint their hair to an appropriate length. The helper needs to add the child's name to each finished painting, with a sentence saying whether the child is tall or short for his or her age. (If they are able to, the children should write these sentences.)

2. The children should complete photocopiable page 42 independently by drawing circles around all the differences between the two pictures.

3. Work with a group of six to eight children, chosen to show clear similarities and differences in their features and size. Describe one child in the group to the other children, and invite them to guess who you are describing. Invite a child to do the same if possible.

4. Set up a table with collage materials for the children to make faces. These can be used to make a border to the display.

5. Organise an adult helper to help the children make handprints and footprints using the resources listed above.

DIFFERENTIATION

Less able children may be unsure of what the words 'similar' and 'different' mean. If possible, use their knowledge of colours to talk about eye colour and then hair colour, encouraging them to notice those in the group with the same or similar-coloured hair or eyes and those with different-coloured hair or eyes.

Introduce the comparative language of size and colour to more able children. For example, ask them: *Who is taller or shorter than Joe? Who has darker hair than me?* Ask them to put the children in the group in order of height, from the tallest to the shortest.

ASSESSMENT

Photocopiable page 42 is intended for the children to complete independently if possible. Keep these sheets as a record of the children's ability to identify differences, if you are sure that they have not copied each other! Group activity 3 provides an opportunity to assess which children can use an understanding of similarities and differences to help identify the person described.

PLENARY

Enlarge a copy of photocopiable page 42 and talk about the differences between the two children. Show the children one or two of the paintings, covering up the name, and ask them to say who is in the picture.

OUTCOMES

● Know that we all have things about us that are the same and things that are different, with particular reference to eye colour, hair colour and size.
● Can investigate similarities and differences through first-hand experience.

LINKS

Across the curriculum: this lesson can be linked to creative development by allowing the children to mix their own skin tone and other colours using red, blue, yellow, white and black paints. Links to personal and social development can be made by allowing the children to talk about and accept the physical differences between us.

Context: GOLDILOCKS AND THE THREE BEARS

The next two lessons make use of the traditional story of 'Goldilocks and the Three Bears'. Other familiar stories are linked to the theme of size, including 'The Three Billy-Goats Gruff' and *The Enormous Crocodile* by Roald Dahl (Puffin).

LESSON 17

OBJECTIVES
● To know that people come in different shapes and sizes.
● To begin to order things according to size.
● To begin to match objects and people according to size.

Vocabulary

large, big, bigger, biggest, small, smaller, smallest, middle-sized

RESOURCES

Main teaching activity: A copy of 'Goldilocks and the Three Bears'. From your collection for Group activity 3, Father Bear's plate, dish and spoon and Baby Bear's chair and bed.
Group activities: 1. A collection of recycled materials, PVA glue, scissors. **2.** A collection of soft toys of various sizes. **3.** A collection of items including spoons, dishes, plates, cups and chairs; beds and pillows in three different sizes (for example, for a doll, baby and adult); a large, medium and small teddy bear; a table. **4.** Toy beds and pillows in three different sizes.

INTRODUCTION

Read the story of 'Goldilocks and the Three Bears'. Spend a few moments going over the story to make sure the children are familiar with it.

MAIN TEACHING ACTIVITY

Talk to the children about the different sizes of the three bears and their belongings. *How do we know which are Father Bear's plate, dish and spoon?* Let the children choose these and give them to the biggest bear. *Which are Baby Bear's chair and bed?* Again, let the children place these by the smallest bear.

Choose and compare two items of the same type (for example, two chairs). Ask the children to show you which is smaller and which is bigger. *Is it the same in our houses? Do we have bigger clothes than our younger brothers and sisters, but smaller clothes than Mum or Dad? Do we have a bigger chair and a bigger bed than a baby has? Why do you think that is?* Explain that as we get older we grow, and that we all come in different shapes and sizes – just like the three bears.

GROUP ACTIVITIES

1. Ask a group of children to use the recycled materials to make beds for Father, Mother and Baby Bear.
 2. Give the children a range of soft toys and let them play with these before putting them in order according to their size. Talk to each child to establish the reason for his or her order. It could be according to girth, height or weight.
 3. Organise a three bears cottage role-play area for the children to set up the bears' breakfast table.
4. Ask a group of children to make the three bears' beds, using the correct-sized pillows, sheets and blankets for each bed.

DIFFERENTIATION

Talk to the more able children about the different shapes and sizes of people and animals. Compare the hands and feet of the children in the group. *Who has the biggest hand and foot? Which bear do you think has the biggest/smallest paw? What size paw does Mother Bear have?* Ask these children to order more than three objects according to their size.

Spend time with the less able children, putting a range of objects in order according to size. Use spoons, bowls, plates, cups and so on.

ASSESSMENT

This lesson deals with the very earliest classification skills of matching and ordering similar objects by size. It is important that you let the children decide on the criteria for their ordering (height, weight and so on). Note the children who are able to match items to the bears correctly according to size. Give the children who cannot do this additional sorting and matching activities to reinforce learning.

PLENARY

Talk to the children about the breakfast table and beds. *How do we know which sheets and pillow to use? Does the biggest bear fit in the smallest bed? Why not?*

OUTCOMES

- Know the comparative language of size.
- Can sort and match items according to size.
- Have begun to classify things according to size.

LINKS

Between units: this lesson links well with the porridge-making activity in Unit 4, Lesson 11.
Across the curriculum: there are several links to numeracy activities in the Goldilocks story, and good opportunities to develop vocabulary for describing size.

LESSON 18

Objectives	• To learn that we all grow. • To find out who are the tallest and shortest children in the class.
Resources	Large sheets or rolls of paper, pencils, paints in a range of colours, Blu-Tack.
Main activity	Talk to the children about how tall they are. Ask three children to stand side by side and compare heights. Use the words 'tallest', 'shortest', 'taller' and 'shorter'. Ask the children who they think is the shortest person in the room. Do they know who is the tallest? Explain that you are going to investigate how tall people are. Put the children into groups of up to four, and give each group a name. Ask them to use large sheets of paper on the floor to draw around each child in turn, then paint pictures of themselves inside the outlines. When they have finished, fix each group's paintings to the wall with Blu-Tack in order of size, and add the group's name. Later in the lesson, mix up the pictures or mix up pictures from different groups; ask each group to restore the correct height order.
Differentiation	Talk to more able children about whether they think the tallest person is the heaviest and the shortest person is the lightest. Find out by weighing whether they were right. Allow less able children to compare two people only. Emphasise that one is 'taller than' or 'shorter than' the other, and continue until they are able to complete this simplified task. If necessary, help them to learn the concept by asking them which of two objects (such as bottles) is taller or shorter.
Assessment	Ask the children questions, including: *Who is the tallest/shortest in your group? Who is taller/shorter than Fred?* Make a note of their answers.
Plenary	Organise the class into height order by asking all the children to stand in a line with a taller child behind them and a shorter child in front. At various times during the day and the week, repeat this activity until you are sure that the children understand it and can do it independently. Change the order of your line from time to time, so that you have the shortest child at the front some days and the tallest child on others. You may also say: *Line up all those who are taller than Fred*, and so on.
Outcomes	• Know that we all grow. • Know that some people grow taller than others. • Know that some people grow faster than others. • Know that we are all different heights.

LESSON 19

OBJECTIVES

● To find out how many parts of the body the children can name.
● To assess whether the children understand that we all grow and change as we become older.
● To assess whether the children can identify simple similarities and differences between people.

RESOURCES

Introduction: A large picture of a child, Post-it notes, a felt-tipped pen, Blu-Tack.
Assessment activities: 1. A computer and a copy of *My World*, a printer. **2.** Photocopiable page 43, scissors, adhesive sticks, paper. **3.** Photocopiable page 44, pencils.

PREPARATION

Write some of the names of parts of the body onto Post-it notes. Set up the computer with a copy of *My World*. Make one copy per child of each of the two photocopiable sheets.

INTRODUCTION

Work with a group of eight children. Ask them to point to and name a part of their own body that they know. Write the name on a Post-it note and stick it onto a large picture of a child displayed on the wall beside you. Continue until the children have named as many parts as they can. If you start with less able children, each group that follows can be challenged to think of less obvious parts of the body.

MAIN ASSESSMENT ACTIVITY

Ask an adult helper to work with pairs of children on the computer, matching labels to parts of the body. The helper can act as a reader, and help the children to add their names and print out their labelled pictures.

ASSESSMENT ACTIVITY 2

Ask the children to complete photocopiable page 43 by cutting out the six pictures and arranging them in the correct order to show a person getting older.

ASSESSMENT ACTIVITY 3

Ask the children to complete photocopiable page 44. This sheet asks them to draw pictures of themselves as babies and as they look now.

Assessment outcomes

On completion of these lessons and Assessment activities, you should know which children have attained the scientific aspects of the following early learning goals in knowledge and understanding of the world:
● Investigate fruit and other objects using all five senses.
● Find out, recognise and identify some of the features of humans.
● Understand the changes that occur in humans as we get older.
● Look closely at similarities and differences between human beings.

Name

Looking closely

Match the fruit.

before

after

What are they like?

pineapple

rough, spiky, knobbly, hard, yellow, green, brown, not soft, not round

orange

rough, squeezable, orange, round, sour

apple

hard, green or red, blemishes, not soft or squeezable, smooth, round, crunchy, sweet, sour

strawberry

soft, juicy, not hard, smooth, sweet

kiwi

spongy, green, furry, soft, itchy, oval

banana

yellow, smooth, long, thin, bendy, spongy, hard or soft

grape

soft, spongy, green or purple, small, round, smooth, juicy

What do they look like?

How do they feel?

Do they have a smell?

Can you think of any words to describe what _____ looks, feels or smells like?

Name

Pineapple

Does it have a smell?

_____

What does it look like? _____

_____

_____

Is it good to touch? Why?_____

_____

_____

Would you like to eat it?_____

_____

_____

Do not touch!

Colour the crosses red.

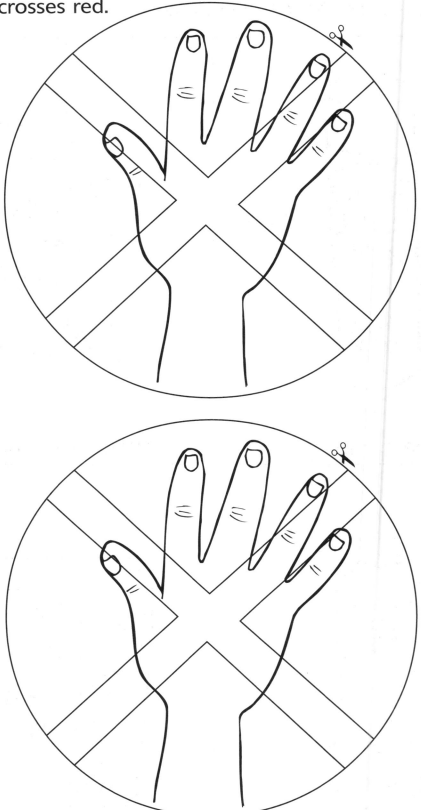

Cut out these pictures and stick them to bottles that you should never touch.

Name

Danger!

Draw a (ring) around the warning signs.

oven cleaner

dishwasher powder

bleach

washing powder

Name

Body parts

Cut out the labels. Stick each label next to the correct body part. Add some more labels of your own.

✂ -

head	leg	foot	hand
arm	finger	body	neck

Match the clothing

UNIT 1 OURSELVES

Name

Two faces

Look at the two faces. Draw a ring around the things that are different.

Give each face a different hair colour. Give each face the same colour eyes.

Name

We all grow

Cut out the pictures and put them in the correct order.

UNIT 1 OURSELVES

This is me!

This is me now.

This is me as a baby.

Looking at animals and plants

ORGANISATION (19 LESSONS)

	OBJECTIVES	MAIN ACTIVITY	GROUP ACTIVITIES	PLENARY	OUTCOMES
LESSON 1	● To learn that there are many different kinds of animal in the world.	Identify some familiar animals and look at their features.	Sort animals by colour and habitat. Sort animals by sounds they make. Paint pictures of animals. Play with toy sets, for example a farm or Noah's Ark. Develop imaginative play using the water tray. Play an animal sound matching game.	Look at one of the completed animal sets and talk about where in the world they live.	● Can recognise and identify animals not previously known. ● Understand that all the animals seen live somewhere in the world. ● Know which animals live with us in our homes and which live on farms, in the sea, in the wild and in other countries. ● Can talk about animals in terms of their size, their colour and the sounds they make.
LESSON 2	● To learn that different animals have different numbers of legs.	Sort animals by the number of legs they have.	Group animals with two, four, six and eight legs on a pictogram. Draw the correct numbers of legs on pictures of animals. Solve animal jigsaws.	Look at the finished pictograms and talk about the animals in each column.	● Have begun to develop the early scientific skill of sorting. ● Can record their findings, with help, in the form of a pictogram. ● Can talk about things that are the same and different in the context of the number of legs that animals have. ● Understand that some animals have the same number of legs, some have no legs and very few have an odd number of legs.
LESSON 3	● To notice differences and similarities between adult animals and their young.	A game to match young and adult animals.		Talk about differences between adult animals and their young.	● Have begun to notice the similarities and differences between young and adult animals. ● Know that baby animals grow into adult animals of the same kind.
LESSON 4	● To learn about the ways that we need to care for our pets. ● To recognise items associated with pet care.	Look at a collection of items used in pet care and identify the purpose of each one.	Set up a 'vets' in the role-play area. Make a large picture of fish in an aquarium. Paint pictures of their favourite pets. Make pictures of pets with collage materials. Make a pet shop in another role-play area.	Make a display of the children's pictures and the pet care items.	● Know how to care for different kinds of pets. ● Know that animals need food and water to stay alive. ● Know that pets need exercise and the correct type of food to stay healthy.
LESSON 5	● To learn that animals move in different ways.	Create a dance using different movements that animals make.		Read the story of 'The Hare and the Tortoise' or sing 'Caterpillars Only Crawl'.	● Know that a particular animal can move in different ways. ● Know some animals move only on the ground, and that some also move in the air. ● Know that how animals move depends on whether they have legs or wings.
LESSON 6	● To learn that some animals have shells.	Look closely at living snails in a tank.		Read 'The Hare and the Tortoise'. Compare the tortoise shell with the snail shell.	● Can recognise a shell on an animal. ● Can talk about how shells are used by different animals.

ORGANISATION (19 LESSONS)

	OBJECTIVES	MAIN ACTIVITY	GROUP ACTIVITIES	PLENARY	OUTCOMES
LESSON 7	● To learn that insects always have six legs. ● To learn that some insects have wings.	Play a game to build up a picture of an insect.	Play the game in small groups. Create a habitat for model insects. Make model insects. Make ladybird pictures. Make symmetrical butterflies.	Discuss the model insects and their features.	● Can talk about insects in terms of their colour, number of legs and whether they can fly. ● Can recognise, identify and name common insects.
LESSON 8	● To learn that spiders have eight legs.	Talk about spiders.	Make models of spiders. Make a spider's web with cotton or wool. Trace or thread a spider's web pattern.	Make a display together of the spiders and webs.	● Know that all spiders have eight legs. ● Know that spiders spin webs in which to catch their prey.
LESSON 9	● To learn that some animals live in water.	Look at models of animals that live in the sea. Sort them by whether they have legs.	Make pictures of fish. Look at similarities and differences between sea animals. Make models of sea animals. Set up imaginative play in the water tray.	Complete a display together.	● Can find similarities and differences between animals that live in the sea. ● Can sort animals according to whether they have legs. ● Can record by drawing what they have found out. ● Know which of various animals live in the sea and which do not.

	OBJECTIVES	MAIN ACTIVITY	ACTIVITIES 2 and 3	OUTCOMES
ASSESSMENT 10	● To assess the children's knowledge of the features of some animals, eg shape and size. ● To assess their ability to: sort familiar animals according to number of legs and where they live; identify an animal from the sound it makes.	Make a pictogram of animals according to the number of legs they have.	Sort animals by the colour or pattern of their coat. Match animal sounds to pictures.	● Can name animals; identify them from the sound they make; identify how many legs they have; sort them by features. ● Can record information in pictograms.

	OBJECTIVES	MAIN ACTIVITY	GROUP ACTIVITIES	PLENARY	OUTCOMES
LESSON 11	● To learn that there are many different green plants. ● To learn that most green plants have stems, leaves, roots, flowers and seeds.	Make posters for the garden centre role-play area. Look carefully at seeds.		Display the children's posters in the garden centre.	● Know that plants grow from seeds. ● Can recognise and identify the stem, leaves, roots, flowers and seeds of a range of flowering plants.
LESSON 12	● To explore plants using the senses of touch, sight and smell.	Explore the scents and textures of plants, developing vocabulary.	Explore the textures of plants. Explore the scents of plants. Plant seeds and plantlets. Role-play a garden centre.	Talk about the children's favourite plants and their reasons.	● Can use the senses of sight, smell and touch to find out about a range of plants, noticing their features, shape, size and colour. ● Can make lists and drawings with support.
LESSON 13	● To identify similarities and differences between two plants.	Note the similarities and differences between two plants.		Note the similarities and differences between another two plants.	● Can develop observational skills by noticing things that are the same and things that are different. ● Can identify the flower, stem, leaves and root of a plant.
LESSON 14	● To learn that seeds grow into plants.	Plant sunflower seeds in pots.	Plant seeds individually, water them and monitor their growth. Look at foods made from sunflowers. Explore compost, pots and garden tools. Role-play a potting shed.	Talk about the care of their seeds and the recording of results.	● Know how to plant and care for seeds. ● Know that plants need water. ● Know that seeds grow into plants.
LESSON 15	● To learn that different plants have different kinds of leaves.	Make lists of similarities and differences between leaves in a collection.	Sort leaves. Describe their features. Print leaf patterns. Make close observational drawings of leaves.	Repeat from Lesson 12, focusing on leaves.	● Know that leaves come in different sizes, shapes and colours. ● Know the features of leaves including veins, edges, top side and underside.

ORGANISATION (19 LESSONS)

	OBJECTIVES	MAIN ACTIVITY	GROUP ACTIVITIES	PLENARY	OUTCOMES
LESSON 16	● To learn that different plants can have different kinds of flowers.	Talk about and explore the flowers and stems on a collection of plants. Paint flowers. Make model flowers. Consider flowers on trees.		Look closely at a flower and consider the role of the pollen.	● Can recognise some features of a flower. ● Understand that flowers come in all shapes and sizes. ● Understand that different flowers have different numbers and shapes of petals. ● Learn that all the petals on the same flower have the same colour and shape. ● Can recognise things that are the same and things that are different.
LESSON 17	● To learn that some plants are safe to eat and others are not.	Sort a range of fruits and vegetables. Consider which parts we eat.	Talk about things that are and are not safe to eat. Role-play a greengrocer's shop. Make pictures of fruit and vegetables.	Create a pictogram with the children's pictures.	● Know that certain parts of a plant can be eaten. ● Know that not all plants can be eaten.
LESSON 18	● To learn that we need to eat in order to stay alive. ● To record information in the form of charts and graphs.	Make a pictorial graph of favourite vegetables.	Make graphs in groups. Make a vegetable snack. Make a model of a healthy meal. Print with vegetables.	Collate the graphs and interpret the results.	● Know that we need to eat in order to stay alive. ● Know that eating certain vegetables is good for you. ● Know that information can be recorded in graphical form.

	OBJECTIVES	ACTIVITIES 1 and 2	3 and 4	OUTCOMES
ASSESSMENT 19	● To assess the children's ability to name the parts of a flowering plant. ● To assess the children's ability to notice similarities and differences between plants, and to sort plants according to noticeable features. ● To assess the children's ability to record their findings by drawing pictures.	Name and label the parts of a flowering plant. Cut out labels and attach them to the correct parts of a plant picture.	Ring the differences between two plant pictures. Sort pictures of plants into sets by whether they have flowers, leaves, stems.	● Can recognise and identify the flower, petals, stem, leaves and roots of a flowering plant ● Know that plants need water to live.

Context: WHERE ANIMALS LIVE

Lessons 1–5 are concerned with places where animals live: a farm, home, pet shop or wildlife park. The children are given opportunities to think about where animals live, both in domestic contexts and in the wild. A computer and TV are used to support the activities.

LESSON 1

OBJECTIVE
● To learn that there are many different kinds of animal in the world.

RESOURCES
Main teaching activity: A video showing different animals; a set of large pictures of different animals; a CD-ROM such as *Amazing Animals* (Dorling Kindersley). Choose pictures relevant to the experience of your children, and some that will extend their learning further.
Group activities: 1 and 4. A set of toy or model animals for the children to play with and sort (these could be a farm, Noah's Ark or zoo animal set); pictures of the same animals to cut out, scissors, adhesive sticks, paper. **2.** Paper and paint in a range of colours. **5.** A water tray. **6.** A cassette recorder and animal sound matching game (either purchased or made in school).
Plenary: The anthology *Apusskidu*, edited by Beatrice Harrop (A&C Black).

PREPARATION
Watch the video and familiarise yourself with the content of the CD-ROM. Put the large pictures into a sequence, starting with the animals with which you think the children are familiar. To provide a collection of animal pictures for cutting out, you can either take various pictures of each type of animal from magazines or use templates to produce identical pictures. You may

Vocabulary
The names of all the animals in your picture collection; stripes, spots, fur, feathers, big, small

wish to start this series of lessons by visiting a local farm that is set up to receive young children as visitors. Please follow your school's policy about visits, especially those involving farms and animals.

INTRODUCTION

Talk to the children about their pets. Does anyone have an animal living with him or her at home? Do any of the children live on a farm? If so, use them as a resource for the introduction. Otherwise, show the children the video and CD-ROM of different animals. Talk about some of the animals seen. *Are they big or small? What colour are they? Do any have stripes, spots, fur or feathers? What sounds do they make?* If the children have touched any of these animals, talk about how the animal's coat felt.

MAIN TEACHING ACTIVITY

Choose your first picture. Ask the children whether they can name the animal. Continue doing this, using pictures of relatively familiar animals, until it is clear that most of the children know the names of the animals being shown. Start to talk about the familiar features of these animals: their size, the sounds they make, their colours and any markings. Now show the children pictures of about six new animals, telling them the animals' names as you do so.

GROUP ACTIVITIES

1. Work with groups of four to six children, talking about the toy animals in your collection. Sort the animals by their colour and then by whether they live with us in our homes, on a farm, in the sea or in the wild (in our country or in other countries).
Allow the children to record their 'Where they live' sets by cutting and sticking pictures
of the animals on to headed pieces of paper.
2. Ask an additional adult to work with groups of four to six children, sorting the toy animals according to the sounds they make.
3. Ask the children to choose an animal they are not familiar with and paint a picture of it independently. Display the pictures in the classroom. You may wish to display these in the context of a story such as 'Noah's Ark'.
4. Let a group of four children play with the toy animal set, such as farm or zoo animals or Noah's Ark. Ask them to arrange the set to make a complete model.
5. Put models of animals that live in water in a water tray for the children to play with.
6. Set up an animal sound matching game for the children to play independently: a recording of an animal sound is played, and the children point to a picture of each animal as they hear it.

DIFFERENTIATION

With more able children, sort the animals that are found in other countries into sets of animals that live in hot and in cold countries. Look on a globe and show the children where these countries can be found. Are there any animals that live in hot *and* cold countries?
With less able children, talk about animals that are found in our country. Start with familiar pets and go on to animals that live on a farm.

ASSESSMENT

Assess whether the children are learning the vocabulary necessary to describe the animals in your collection by listening to their conversations and noting those children who are able to talk about the animals in terms of their features as well as their name and where they live. This will provide you with information concerning the appropriate content and level of the work in the next lesson.

PLENARY

Look at the completed farm, zoo or Noah's Ark and talk about the way the children have organised the animals to make their model. Reinforce the idea that there are many different kinds of animals and that they all live somewhere in our world. Sing 'The Animals Went in Two by Two' (from *Apusskidu*) and other animal songs that you already know.

OUTCOMES

- Can recognise and identify animals not previously known.
- Understand that all the animals seen live somewhere in the world.
- Know which animals live with us in our homes and which live on farms, in the sea, in the wild and in other countries.
- Can talk about animals in terms of their size, their colour and the sounds they make.

LINKS

Across the curriculum: this lesson can be linked to work on communication, language and literacy. Read the children stories and poems to reinforce the names of different animals, such as *The Pig's in the Pond* by Martin Waddell (Walker Books). Talk about whether the animals are really like those in the stories and poems. For example, would real tigers behave like the one in *The Tiger Who Came to Tea* by Judith Kerr (Collins)? You may wish to avoid stories that give the animals a human dimension.

LESSON 2

OBJECTIVES

- To learn that different animals have different numbers of legs.

RESOURCES

Main teaching activity: Pictures and models of several different kinds of animals (a cat, dog, sheep, cow, pig, horse, duck, hen, elephant, giraffe, bird, spider, octopus, insect, snake, snail, tortoise, whale, shark, starfish, worm and fish).
Group activities: 1. Models and pictures of animals (these can be bought from any good educational supplier), an enlarged (A3) copy of photocopiable page 69, Blu-Tack; photocopiable pages 69 and 70, scissors, adhesive sticks. **2.** Photocopiable page 71, pencils. **3.** A range of animal games and jigsaws.

Vocabulary
The names of the animals in your collection; no, none, zero, two, four, five, six, eight, legs

PREPARATION

Make an enlarged copy of page 69 to use for demonstration.

INTRODUCTION

Sit the children in a circle around the collection of animal models and pictures. Show these to the children, and pass the models around so that the children can play with them. Find out whether they know the names of all the animals in your collection. Keep those that the children are familiar with, and either teach them the names of some of the others or remove these from the activity at this stage.

MAIN TEACHING ACTIVITY

Choose a familiar animal, such as a dog or cat. Show the children a model or picture of that animal and ask them what they can see. Ask questions such as: *What colour is the animal? Are all cats the same colour, or can they be different colours? How many legs does the animal have? Do all cats have four legs?* Ask the children to find all the other animals that have four legs in your collection.

Now ask the children to choose another animal. Discuss the number of legs, the animal's size and the colour and pattern of its coat. Again, ask the children to find all the animals that have the same number of legs. Continue with other animals in your collection until you are sure the children are looking carefully at the number of legs.

GROUP ACTIVITIES

1. Work with a group of six children, looking at the models and pictures of animals. Ask the children to find all the animals that have four legs and put them together in a row or line. Repeat the activity with the animals that have two, six and eight legs. *Do any of the animals have one, three or seven legs? How many animals have five legs? Do any have no legs?* As you sort the animals, tell the children their names (if they do not already know them). Show the children the enlarged copy of page 69. To one of the numbered columns, attach a picture of an animal with the same number of legs (for example, a beetle in column 6). Give each child copies of photocopiable page 70. Ask them to cut out the pictures of animals, sort them according to the number of legs, then stick them down on a copy of page 69 to make a large pictogram. Discuss any pictures that they cannot place. Ask them to add to the pictogram with their own

100 SCIENCE LESSONS ● **YEAR R / UNIT 2**

49

UNIT 2 ANIMALS & PLANTS

drawings over the next few days. Show them how to label the pictogram appropriately.

2. Talk to the children about odd and even numbers in a numeracy lesson. Give them copies of photocopiable page 71, which contains pictures of different animals without legs. Ask them to draw on the legs. They will soon realise that the legs are placed in pairs, on opposite sides of the body. Many animals have four or six legs, and very few animals have an odd number of legs (for example, the starfish).

3. Allow groups of four children to play with the different animal games and jigsaws you have provided.

DIFFERENTIATION

Give less able children two animals and ask them whether these animals have the same number of legs before asking them to find all the animals with two and then four legs. Some of these children may understand the concept of nought, and be able to find all the animals in your collection with no legs.

More able children could be asked to talk about how the animals use their legs to move, and the length and positions of their legs, before finding the animals with more than four legs. Challenge them to find an animal with one, three, five or seven legs.

ASSESSMENT

Make a record of the investigative skills the children have developed, including sorting animals by their number of legs. Note those who are able to talk about what they have done. Keep the children's pictograms as evidence of their ability to make simple recordings of their findings.

PLENARY

Talk about the children's pictograms. *How many animals have we found with four legs, six legs, no legs, eight legs, five legs? How many animals have more than four legs? Are there more animals with four legs than with eight legs?*

OUTCOMES

● Have begun to develop the early scientific skill of sorting.
● Can record their findings, with help, in the form of a pictogram.
● Can talk about things that are the same and different in the context of the number of legs that animals have.
● Understand that some animals have the same number of legs, some have no legs and very few have an odd number of legs.

LINKS

Across the curriculum: this lesson provides a good context for counting activities.

LESSON 3

Objective	To notice differences and similarities between adult animals and their young.
Resources	Photographs of the children's pets; pictures of adult cats and dogs and of puppies and kittens.
Main activity	Ask the children who have a dog, cat, puppy or kitten at home to talk about it. Invite them to tell you their pet's name, its colour, what it likes to do and so on. If they have a photograph of their pet, ask them to bring this in and pass it around the group. Discuss the pets' names. Sometimes a name is chosen because of an animal's colour or because of other features. This may provide opportunities to develop speaking and listening skills. Show the children a picture of an adult dog. Talk about the features of the dog. Ask questions such as: *How many legs does it have? What is its colour?* Next, show the children a picture of a puppy. *Does the puppy look the same?* Talk about all the ways the puppy looks the same and all the ways it looks different. Repeat the activity with the pictures of the cat and kitten.
Differentiation	Introduce pictures of other familiar animals to more able children and ask them to match the adult animals to their young. Talk to less able children in smaller groups, and talk about one kind of animal in each activity session. Allow them to make a display showing the adult animal correctly matched to their young. Add words to describe the similarities and differences between young and adult animals.
Assessment	Most children will note the differences in the animal's size, colour and shape, and the fact that the numbers of eyes, ears and legs are the same. Note those children who are able to notice less obvious differences, such as the texture of the coat or the shape of the head.
Plenary	Talk to the children about what they have found out about young and adult animals. Look at pictures of an adult dog or cat and the corresponding young animal; agree on and ring the differences between them.
Outcomes	Have begun to notice the similarities and differences between young and adult animals. Know that baby animals grow into adult animals of the same kind.

LESSON 4

OBJECTIVES
- To learn about the ways that we need to care for our pets.
- To recognise items associated with pet care.

RESOURCES

Main teaching activity: A collection of items that are used in pet care. Include brushes for grooming; food and water dishes and bottles, food items (such as carrots, fish food, greens and pet food containers); leads, collars and name tags; pet toys and pet homes (such as sleep baskets and fish tanks). Someone may be able to bring in a pet passport.
Group activities: 2 and 3. Paints in a range of colours, paper. **4.** A range of collage materials, scissors, adhesive sticks, paper. **5.** Photographs of the children's pets.
Plenary: A display surface and display board; cardboard boxes of different sizes, pieces of fabric, a stapler.

Vocabulary

soft, fluffy, small, bigger, feed, groom, wash, exercise

PREPARATION

Cover a display board with suitable backing paper. Organise several cardboard boxes along the surface in front to create different display heights, and cover them with fabric (stapled in place). Ask the children to bring in items used in pet care and photographs of their pets (see Resources). Make sure that any pet food containers shown are well washed out, empty and safe. Invite a child or parent to talk to the class about a pet and show a photograph of it (see Introduction).

INTRODUCTION

Tell the children that you are going to think about all the things that are needed to look after different kinds of pets. Ask a child or parent to talk about a pet. Encourage him or her to explain what the pet eats, where it lives, how often it has to be fed, watered and washed or groomed. Alternatively, talk about your own pet if you have one. Show a photograph of the pet being talked about if possible.

MAIN TEACHING ACTIVITY

Show the children some of the things in your pet care collection. Ask whether anyone can say what each item is used for. Talk about the need to feed different pets the correct food. For example, rabbits, hamsters and guinea-pigs need plenty of greens to eat, and water should also be available, especially on hot days. Talk about the importance of exercise when showing a dog's lead or a hamster's exercise wheel. Encourage the children to talk about the ways that pets play.

GROUP ACTIVITIES

1. Talk to groups of six children about the care of different pets. Set up a role-play situation where the children are taking their pet to the vet with a variety of complaints, such as toothache or being overweight. Ask the children how the pet can be cured, encouraging them to refer to the correct type of food and exercise.

2. Organise a group of ten children to make a large painting of some tropical fish or goldfish in an aquarium. Talk about the pets that live in water: fish, frogs, newts and so on.

3. Give the children paints in a range of colours and ask them to make pictures of their favourite pets for the display.

4. Set up a table with collage materials and ask an additional adult to help the children make pictures of rabbits, hamsters, cats and dogs.

5. Make a pet shop role-play area with the various pet care items. Ask the children each to find everything that a particular pet needs to keep it healthy.

DIFFERENTIATION

With more able children, make a pictogram to show the variety of pets owned by the children in the class. Find out from this information which is the most popular kind of pet.

Work with less able children to look first at kittens and then at puppies. Be very specific about the needs of these pets, and ask the children what is meant by 'exercise'. Talk through a puppy's need to go for long walks and a kitten's need to have clean fur.

ASSESSMENT

Note whether the children find the correct or incorrect things for their pet in the pet shop. For example, do they choose cat food for a rabbit, or a dog lead for a cat?

PLENARY

Make the display together. Staple the children's pictures and photographs to the display board, and display the pet care items on the boxes. Add appropriate labels.

OUTCOMES

● Know how to care for different kinds of pets.
● Know that animals need food and water to stay alive.
● Know that pets need exercise and the correct type of food to stay healthy.

LINKS

Between units: this lesson is linked to Unit 1, Lesson 5 on how humans stay healthy and need food and water to stay alive.
Across the curriculum: the graph of favourite pets links to data-handling in the context of numeracy.

LESSON 5

Objective	● To learn that animals move in different ways.
Resources	Video clips of various animals moving; a cassette player and recording of *Peter and the Wolf* by Prokofiev, or any music that can be used to suggest the different movements of animals (such as *Carnival of the Animals* by Saint-Saëns); pictures and models of animals (see Main activity); a copy of *Aesop's Fables* or *Harlequin* edited by David Gadsby and Beatrice Harrop (A&C Black).
Main activity	Before the lesson, show the children video clips of different animals moving and introduce some vocabulary that describes the animals' movements. Show the children a picture of a cat and play the relevant extract from *Peter and the Wolf*. Talk about the way the cat moves, using the words 'walk', 'run', 'jump' and 'creep'. Ask the children: *Does the cat move quickly or slowly, or both? Does it move close to the floor? Can it fly? Can it swim?* Let the children move to the music in their own way; afterwards, for a short time, let them evaluate and improve their performance. Repeat the activity for the other animals depicted in the music (including the flying bird, the duck and the wolf), using the words 'fly', 'swoop', 'hop', 'walk' and 'hover'. If you use other music, adapt the selection of animals as appropriate.
Differentiation	With more able children, include video clips of animals with particular movements – for example, horses galloping and trotting; lizards crawling and stretching. Talk to less able children about the parts of the body that the animals use to move.
Assessment	Working with small groups, show the children pictures of animals and ask them to depict (by describing or acting out) each animal's movement. Include a spider, snake, kangaroo and snail as well as more familiar animals such as a dog, cat, bird and rabbit.
Plenary	Read Aesop's fable 'The Hare and the Tortoise' to the children, or sing 'Caterpillars Only Crawl' from *Harlequin*.
Outcomes	● Know that a particular animal can move in different ways. ● Know some animals move only on the ground, and that some also move in the air. ● Know that how animals move depends on whether they have legs or wings.

Context: STORIES AND RHYMES

The next five lessons can be taught through the context of stories and rhymes, many of which are traditional and/or will be familiar to the children. They can also be used for text-level work in literacy lessons.

LESSON 6

Objective	● To learn that some animals have shells.
Resources	A glass tank half-filled with compost and leaves, with some small twigs and wood from branches placed on the top; a collection of live snails; pictures of other animals that have a shell; paper, pencils, paints; a copy of *Aesop's Fables*.
Main activity	Collect some snails from the school grounds the day before this lesson, and place them in the prepared tank. Talk to the children about the snails. Explain that you found them all in the school grounds – and that once the children have finished looking at them, you will return them to the place where they were found. Explain the need to take great care of the snails while they are in your classroom. Talk about how the snails are moving. *Do they have any legs?* Talk about the shell and what the snail uses it for. Ask a child to point to the shell. *Why does the snail always carry it around?* Show the pictures and talk about other animals that have shells, including crabs, mussels and tortoises. *Do they all use the shell in the same way?* (They all use it to hide in, but some have a shell that closes entirely and others do not.) Ask the children to point to the shell of each animal in your pictures. Ask them to draw and paint pictures of the snails and other animals that have a shell. Display these in your classroom.
Differentiation	With more able children, look more closely at the pictures of various shelled animals. Make simple comparisons between the size, shape and colour of the different shells. Give less able children many opportunities to observe the snails and talk about what they can see (particularly the shell). Tempt the snails to eat by placing food a little way away, so that the snail has to move to reach the food.
Assessment	Note whether the children's pictures represent the shell accurately. Note those children who can talk about the shape and size of the shell and the way that the animal hides in it when it is disturbed.
Plenary	Read 'The Hare and the Tortoise' from *Aesop's Fables*. Talk about the tortoise shell and how it is similar to and different from the snail shell.
Outcomes	● Can recognise a shell on an animal. ● Can talk about how shells are used by different animals.

LESSON 7

OBJECTIVES
● To learn that insects always have six legs.
● To learn that some insects have wings and can fly.

RESOURCES

Main teaching activity: Dice with numbers 1–6; photocopiable page 72, adhesive, card; commercial pictures and models of insects, including an ant, ladybird, wasp and bee.
Group activities: 1. Photocopiable pages 73 and 74, adhesive, card. **2.** Models of insects, a sand pit or sand tray, wood and stones. **3.** Recycled and collage materials, scissors, PVA glue.
4 and 5. Red paint, card, black sugar paper, scissors, adhesive.

Vocabulary

head, legs, six, body (thorax, abdomen), eyes, antenna

PREPARATION

Make six copies of page 72, glue to thick card and cut out the legs, body and head of the ant. Make similar insects from copies of pages 73 and 74 to extend the game. Change your dice so that it has two '1' faces by blanking out five of the spots on the '6' face.

INTRODUCTION

Show the children the models and pictures of insects. Talk about the colour, shape and features of each one. Can the children see the eyes, legs and wings? Ask them why some insects can fly and others cannot. Do they know it is because some insects have wings and others do not? Sort the insects into those that can fly and those that cannot. Next, show the children a model or picture of an ant. Talk about its head, eyes, body and legs. Count the legs together. Show the children the antennae and their position on the head.

MAIN TEACHING ACTIVITY

Sit the children in a circle and play the dice game together, using your enlarged ant picture and body parts. The children should take turns to throw the dice. Each number corresponds to a different part of the body: 5 gets the thorax and abdomen, 4 the head, 3 an antenna, 2 an eye and 1 a leg. The first child to make up a complete ant wins. Play several times.

GROUP ACTIVITIES

 1. Ask an adult helper to play the dice game, using a beetle (see page 73) with a group of four to six children. The helper should reinforce how many legs the beetle has.
 2. Put stones, pieces of wood and some of the model insects into the sand pit or sand tray, and invite the children to make a home for the insects. Talk about which insects can fly and which cannot.
 3. Use a range of collage and recycled materials to make models of different insects with the children. You may wish to suspend these from the ceiling or among large leaves arranged on a display board.
 4. Make large ladybirds with the children from card, red paint and black paper dots. Cut down the centre almost to the end of each one, and open the wings slightly (see diagram). Glue a piece of black sugar paper under the opened wings on the body.
 5. Use paint and the folding technique (as above) to make butterflies with the children.

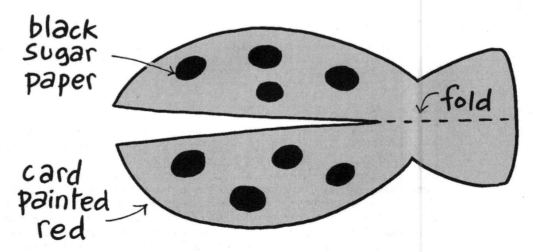

black sugar paper

card painted red

fold

DIFFERENTIATION

Talk to more able children about the hard shell that covers the wings and body of the ladybird. Play the game again, using the ladybird version (see page 74). A few children may be ready to learn the names of the three major insect body parts – the head, thorax and abdomen – in which case you can play the game with the number 6 getting the abdomen and 5 getting the thorax.

ASSESSMENT

Note those children who are able to talk about the different insects in terms of colour, size and number of legs, and those who know which insects can fly and which cannot.

PLENARY

Display the model insects that the children have made. Ask one or two to talk about their model, explaining how they made it and why they painted it the colour they have. Count the number of legs on each model and identify those that can fly.

OUTCOMES

● Can talk about insects in terms of their colour, number of legs and whether they can fly.
● Can recognise, identify and name common insects.

LINKS

Across the curriculum: read the children stories and rhymes about common insects, including *The Bad-tempered Ladybird* by Eric Carle (Puffin) and the traditional nursery rhyme 'Ladybird, Ladybird, Fly Away Home'.

LESSON 8

OBJECTIVE

● To learn that spiders have eight legs.

RESOURCES

Main teaching activity: A picture of a spider; a large picture of a spider's web (see Preparation); black tissue paper, adhesive tape, pipe-cleaners, blue paper circles, black wool or cotton.
Group activities: 1. As for Main teaching activity. **2.** Sequins and offcuts of shiny paper, adhesive, glitter pens. **3.** Black cotton or wool, art straws, adhesive. **4.** Photocopiable page 75, pencils (or card, a hole punch and wool).

Vocabulary

web, spider, eight legs, body

PREPARATION

Use white paint on black paper to make a large picture of a spider's web (A2 or the size of the display board).

INTRODUCTION

Sing 'Incey Wincey Spider' together, adding actions to the words. Talk about what happens to the spider in the song. Ask: *Have you ever washed a spider down the bath plughole at home? Can you think of another way to get the spider out of the bath?*

MAIN TEACHING ACTIVITY

Show the children a picture of a spider. Count the number of legs together. Talk about the children's perceptions of spiders (be sensitive to any children who have a fear of spiders). Explain that you are going to make a large display of spiders for the classroom. Show them your picture of a spider's web, and talk about the reason why spiders spin webs. Say that some children will help to decorate the web so that it sparkles as if on a frosty morning (see overleaf). Show the children how to make spiders by screwing up an A3 piece of black tissue paper into an oval shape and fixing in the ends with sticky tape. Use eight pipe-cleaners (or strips of black sugar paper) to make the legs, fixing them to the body with sticky tape before adding two blue paper circles for eyes. Attach a length of black wool or cotton to suspend the spider from the ceiling.

GROUP ACTIVITIES

1. Work with groups of four to make a spider in the same way as the Main teaching activity, until every child has made a spider.

2. Ask an adult helper to work with a group of children, decorating the spider's web by gluing sequins and offcuts of shiny paper to the white lines on the web. Some children may wish to use glitter pens to add circles of colour along the lines.

3. Work with groups to make spider's webs by winding black cotton or wool around circular constructions of art straws (see illustration). Suspend the webs among the spiders.

4. Use photocopiable page 75 as a tracing activity, or make it into a threading activity by mounting copies on card and punching holes at the intersections for the children to thread wool through.

DIFFERENTIATION

Invite more able children to find out about the octopus, another animal with eight legs.

Together, make a collection of objects that have eight of something (for example, eight pencils in a jar). Work with less able children individually when they are making the spiders, so that you can count the number of legs together as they are added to the models.

ASSESSMENT

Note which children know that spiders have eight legs, and are able to add eight legs to their spider models.

PLENARY

Make the display together. Staple the finished web to a display board before fixing some spiders onto the web and suspending others from the ceiling, interspersed with the wool and straw webs. Use some webs and spiders, along with the threading cards, to make a frame for the finished picture. Reinforce the fact that spiders have eight legs.

OUTCOMES

● Know that all spiders have eight legs.
● Know that spiders spin webs in which to catch their prey.

LINKS

Between units: this lesson can be linked to the creation of the Little Miss Muffet display in Unit 6, Lesson 1.
Across the curriculum: the children have opportunities to develop manual skills when completing the spider's web sewing card and web-winding activities.

LESSON 9

OBJECTIVES

● To learn that some animals live in water.

RESOURCES

Main teaching activity: A display board, blue and green paper, blue and green crêpe or tissue paper, adhesive, white paint; a copy of *The Rainbow Fish* by Marcus Pfister (North-South Books); pictures and models of animals that live in the sea; goldfish in a tank; salt, water, a beaker.
Group activities: 1. Fish shapes cut from paper, scissors, offcuts of coloured papers, PVA glue.
2. Paper, pencils. **3.** Recycled materials, adhesive sticks, scissors. **4.** A water tray, blue food colouring, ice cubes or lumps.
Plenary: Paper labels, thin cotton.

PREPARATION

Cover a display board with blue and green paper, and staple strips of blue and green crêpe and tissue paper across the top to represent waves. Add touches of white paint to the tops of the 'waves'.

INTRODUCTION

Read the story *The Rainbow Fish* by Marcus Pfister. Talk to the children about the fish mentioned in this story. Show the children the goldfish in your tank, and talk about their features.

MAIN TEACHING ACTIVITY

Show the children the model animals in your collection. Tell them that all of these creatures live in the sea. Find out which children have been to the seaside. Explain that sea water is like other water, but is salty. You may wish to show those who have never been to the seaside what 'salt water' is by dissolving some table salt in a beaker of water.

Sort the animals into two groups: those that have legs and those that do not. Ask: *What do you notice about the animals that have no legs?* (They have fins and a tail.) *How are they different from those that have legs?* (Those with legs do not have fins.) *How many of the animals have eyes?* (All of them.)

Talk about how these animals manage to live in the water. For example, explain that fish need to be in the water all of the time: they will die on land. Other animals, such as dolphins and whales, need to go to the surface of the water every so often to take a large breath of air. Ask the children whether they know of any other animals that live in the sea.

GROUP ACTIVITIES

1. Organise the children into groups of six to make pictures of fish. Give each child a paper fish shape, and show the children how to cut and stick circles and stripes to make colourful fish like the ones in the story. The finished fish pictures can be stapled to the display.
2. Work with groups of four or six children to talk about the similarities and differences between the animals that live in the sea. Ask the children to compare two of the animals and record what they notice by drawing them.
3. Ask an adult helper to work with the children, making other model animals to go in your display (such as an octopus, dolphin, whale, starfish, crab or shark).
4. Add blue food colouring and ice cubes or lumps to the water in the water tray to encourage imaginative play with the collection of sea creature models.

DIFFERENTIATION

Talk to more able children about other kinds of water environment, such as rivers and ponds. Talk about some of the animal life in these environments.

With less able children it is best to take one animal at a time, asking the children to make a model or draw a picture of each one as you talk about its features.

ASSESSMENT

In the Plenary, hold up various pictures of animals and ask children to say whether they live in the sea or not. Note those children who can distinguish between marine creatures and similar land-living animals such as a snail or a woodlouse.

PLENARY

Finish the display together, adding labels for the animals' features (fins, claws and so on). Attach some model animals to thin cotton and suspend them in front of the display to create a 3-D effect. Place your pictures of animals in front of the display for the children to sort every day into two groups.

OUTCOMES

● Can find similarities and differences between animals that live in the sea.
● Can sort animals according to whether they have legs.
● Can record by drawing what they have found out.
● Know which of various animals live in the sea and which do not.

LINKS

Across the curriculum: this lesson links well with creative development. Let the children paint and collage pictures of fish. In a dance lesson, create a dance about the movement of fish using the music 'Aquarium' from *The Carnival of the Animals* by Saint-Saëns. The children could also compose a musical accompaniment to their dance, or to a poem, using pitched and non-pitched percussion instruments.

ASSESSMENT

LESSON 10

OBJECTIVES

● To assess the children's knowledge of the features of some animals, such as their shape and size and the colour and pattern of their coat.
● To assess the children's ability to sort familiar animals into sets according to their number of legs and where they live.
● To assess the children's ability to identify an animal from the sound that it makes.

RESOURCES

Assessment activities: 1. A set (Set A) of pictures of familiar animals, including a dog, cat, cow, pig, fish, bird, spider, snake, ladybird, ant and worm. **2.** A set (Set B) of pictures of animals that have a distinctive colouring and/or pattern, such as a tiger, elephant, horse, monkey, rabbit, leopard, zebra, giraffe, spotted and stripy fish, butterfly and ladybird (you may wish to include cows, dogs and pigs with spots); a set (Set C) of pictures of animals that live in different environments, including a whale, dolphin, crab, starfish and snail. **3.** An audio tape with different animal sounds; a matching set (Set D) of pictures.

PREPARATION

Organise the Assessment activities around the classroom, depending on the number of adult helpers you have available. Prepare a chart for the pictogram in Assessment activity 1.

INTRODUCTION

Show the children the animal pictures in Set A. Ask them to name the animals. Ask questions such as: *Can you tell me how many legs each of the animals has? Can you tell me any other animals with the same number of legs? Can anyone show me how this animal moves? Why can't the snake walk?* (Because it doesn't have legs.)

MAIN ASSESSMENT ACTIVITY

Ask the children to organise the pictures in Set A into a pictogram according to the number of legs each animal has. Invite them to add to the collection of animal pictures by drawing some of their own. This makes the activity open-ended and allows the children to show you how well they understand the concept.

ASSESSMENT ACTIVITY 2

With groups of up to six children, sort the pictures in Set B according to the animal's colour or pattern. Note those children who can separate the stripy animals from the spotted ones. Which children recognise that the elephant has no distinctive coat markings? How many can name another animal that has no distinctive coat markings, such as the hippopotamus, the rhinoceros or the lion? Go on to sort the pictures in Set C according to where the animals live: in the ground, on the shore, in the sea and so on. Note which children know, or can predict sensibly, where an animal lives (for example, a whale lives in the sea rather than in rivers or on the shore).

ASSESSMENT ACTIVITY 3

Play an audio tape of animal sounds, and ask the children to identify which animal is making each sound by holding up the matching picture from Set D.

Assessment outcomes

On completion of these Assessment activities, you should know which children have attained the following objectives linked to knowledge and understanding of the world:
● Identify the names of familiar animals and those learned in this set of lessons.
● Identify familiar animals from the sound they make.
● Identify how many legs various types of animal have.
● Sort animals by visible features.
● Record information in pictograms.

Context: ROLE-PLAY

The next eight lessons involve the use of the role-play area as a greengrocer's shop or a garden centre. Many of the play activities suggested in these lessons are set within this area, and provide the starting points for other learning activities suggested under Links.

LESSON 11

Objective	● To learn that there are many different green plants. ● To learn that most green plants have stems, leaves, roots, flowers and seeds.
Resources	Lots of empty seed packets and some containing a few seeds (make sure they have not been dressed with insecticide); pot plants, flowers, vegetables; a picture of a tree; books about plants, including *The Tiny Seed* by Eric Carle (Puffin); posters showing plants; a collection of other items (such as a trowel, flowerpots, a watering can, seed trays, a sieve, seed compost, various seeds) that can be bought from a garden centre; paper, pencils and paints. You may wish to link this lesson to a visit to a local garden centre.
Main activity	Explain that you are going to set up a garden centre in the role-play area. Show the children what you already have for this. Talk about the kinds of things you will find at the garden centre. Together, make posters of things that can be bought from the garden centre – particularly plants and flowers. Talk about the roots, stems, leaves and flowers on the plants before asking the children to draw and paint pictures of some of the plants. Tell the children that the plants always make seeds, so that more plants of the same kind will grow. Show them the seed packets. Talk about the pictures on the packets, then show the children some of the seeds. *Does the seed look anything like the picture?* Allow them to marvel at the fact that such a large and beautiful plant grows from such a small and simple seed. Read out *The Tiny Seed* by Pat Hutchins.
Differentiation	With more able children, look at the different seeds. Reach some conclusions about whether the tiniest seed produces the smallest plant, and so on. Allow less able children to plant some fast-growing seeds such as cress, mustard or birdseed. When these are grown, talk about the different parts.
Assessment	From the children's drawings, note whether they have included all the parts of the plant or flower and drawn them in the correct places.
Plenary	Display the children's pictures and posters around the role-play area. Arrange some of the plants and other items you have collected in the 'garden centre'.
Outcomes	● Know that plants grow from seeds. ● Can recognise and identify the stem, leaves, roots, flowers and seeds of a range of flowering plants.

LESSON 12

OBJECTIVE
● To explore plants using the senses of touch, sight and smell.

RESOURCES

Main teaching activity: A cactus (not too spiky!), Christmas pine, spider plant, rosemary plant, ornamental garden grass, holly, ivy, laurel, mint plant, lemon plant, curry plant, lavender, heather; flowers with textured stems (such as carnation, rose, busy lizzie and daffodil) and distinctive smells (such as freesias, pineapple broom and orange blossom); an orange, mint sauce, curry powder, pineapple juice, lemon juice.
Group activities: As above; plant pots.

PREPARATION

Cut some of the thorns from the rose stem. Check for any allergies, and make sure that children liable to be affected do not come into contact with the plants. Check your LEA list of plants that should not be used.

INTRODUCTION

Show the children all the plants in your collection and talk about what one or two of them look like. Talk about the size, shape and colour of the leaves, stem, flower (if any) and roots (if visible). Put the plants into sets according to whether they have leaves, then whether they have flowers.

MAIN TEACHING ACTIVITY

Choose one or two of the plants that smell, and pass them one at a time around the group for the children to smell. Ask the children what these smells remind them of. Pass around the items whose smells match the plants: curry powder with the curry plant, mint sauce with the mint and so on. Encourage the children to think of words to describe the smells: 'sweet', 'spicy', 'makes you sneeze' and so on.

Repeat the activity with plants that have different textures, such as the Christmas pine and busy lizzie, and talk about how they feel. Encourage the children to think of words to describe textures: 'thick', 'thin', 'long', 'short', 'tickly', 'soft', 'rough', 'smooth' and so on.

GROUP ACTIVITIES

1. Work with groups of four children to explore the texture of some of the plants in the collection. This will allow you to keep an eye on the rose and cactus touching, which could be a problem if not supervised closely. Ask the children to put the plants into sets according to their texture. Encourage them to use words such as 'hard', 'spiky', 'prickly' and 'smooth'.
2. Ask an adult helper to work with a group of children to explore various plants and plant-derived items by using the sense of smell. The helper should discuss the scent made by each plant with the children, asking them whether these scents remind them of anything before passing the items around for them to smell.

3. Allow a group of children to plant seeds (in pots or trays), set out the plants and buy and sell in the 'garden centre' role-play area. A parent helper would be useful to support this activity.
4. If your spider plant has small plantlets, plant these in pots for the children to look after in their 'garden centre'.

Vocabulary

spiky, smooth, tickly, soft, dry, thick, thin, long, short, rough, textured, smell, scent, sharp, shiny, dull, sweet, spicy, sneeze (aroma, perfume)

DIFFERENTIATION

Organise more able children into one group and work with them on making observational drawings. Ask them to focus closely on the leaves and their position on the plants. Sort the pictures into sets: plants with leaves and plants without.

Explore three plants with a group of less able children, encouraging them to use all their senses. List everything they say about their discoveries. Use this recording to assess their knowledge and use of language.

ASSESSMENT

Note those children who use their senses to explore and find things out about the plants in your collection (see Differentiation above). Note those children who are beginning to make simple comparisons between features of different plants, such as leaf shape or scent.

PLENARY

Ask one group to choose their favourite plant from the collection. Can they say why this is their favourite? Encourage them to talk about what they can see, feel and touch. Reinforce the learning objective: we can find out about plants by using our senses.

OUTCOMES

● Can use the senses of sight, smell and touch to find out about a range of plants, noticing their features, shape, size and colour.
● Can make lists and drawings with support.

LINKS

Between units: this lesson links to work on looking after plants in Unit 3.

LESSON 13

Objective	● To identify similarities and differences between two plants.
Resources	A flowering plant (such as a chrysanthemum), a non-flowering plant (such as a spider plant or Christmas pine), magnifying lenses; a prepared drawing of two plants for comparison (see Differentiation). Check for any allergies, and make sure that children liable to be affected do not come into contact with the plants.
Main activity	Show the children the non-flowering plant and talk about its shape, size and colour. Note the shape, size and colour of the leaves. *Are they long or short, fat or thin? Are they dark green or light green? Do they have straight or curved edges?* Repeat this activity to describe the flowering plant. Ask the children to point out things about the two plants that are the same. (For example, they both have leaves, roots and stems; they are both growing and need looking after.) Ask groups of children to look carefully at the two plants. First of all, they should look at the features that are different – for example, one has flowers and the other does not; one has several colours (flowers, leaves and stem) and the other is mostly green. They should use magnifying lenses to look carefully at the leaves. Note down all the differences that the children describe, such as the length, breadth, shape and colour of the leaves.
Differentiation	With less able children, choose two different plants and look for things that are the same and different about them. Ask the children to show the differences by colouring a prepared drawing of the two plants under your direction. You could use bowls of bulbs, such as yellow daffodils and purple crocuses – this will give the children clear differences of colour and size to focus on, and it will be easy for them to colour the differences. Let more able children choose their own plants to repeat the activity independently. Use their recordings for assessment purposes.
Assessment	Ask an adult helper to write down what the children say as they point out the similarities and differences between the plants. Focused observation of more able children working independently will provide a good opportunity for this. Also see Differentiation, above.
Plenary	Repeat the activity with another two different plants, either chosen by you to reinforce a particular point picked up during the lesson (through assessment) or chosen by the children. The children may need to pick out different plants from a wider selection for each feature they notice, and some will need to repeat the same idea with different plants.
Outcomes	● Can develop observational skills by noticing things that are the same and things that are different. ● Can identify the flower, stem, leaves and root of a plant.

LESSON 14

OBJECTIVE

● To learn that seeds grow into plants.

RESOURCES

Main teaching activity: Sunflower seeds, a sunflower head (optional), plant pots, seed compost, a lollipop stick.
Group activities: 1. Plant pots, seed compost, lollipop sticks, felt-tipped pens, a sunny spot in the classroom; a digital camera (if possible). **2.** Paper, pencils. **3.** A collection of foods made with sunflower seeds (such as margarine, oil, cake). **4.** A sand tray, seed compost, water; some pots, trowels and forks. **5.** Other plant seeds, plant pots, seed compost.
Plenary: Photocopiable page 76, pencils.

Vocabulary

sunflower, seed, plant, plant pot, seed compost, grow, growth

PREPARATION

The best time for planting these seeds is in March or April. Avoid planting them close to the holidays, when the children will miss the first signs of growth.

INTRODUCTION

Show the children the sunflower head, if you have one. Alternatively, show and pass around the sunflower seeds.

MAIN TEACHING ACTIVITY

Give each child a sunflower seed and talk about the colour, shape and size of the seeds. Show the children how to press a seed into seed compost in a plant pot. Explain why you are planting two in each pot. (In case one doesn't grow.) Talk about how the children will need to care for the plant when it begins to grow. Write your name on a lollipop stick and show the children how to stick this into the pot. Discuss where would be a good place to put the pot so that you can keep an eye on the plant and look after it.

GROUP ACTIVITIES

1. Rotating groups of four children, allow every child in the class to plant two sunflower seeds. Write each child's name on a lollipop stick and add it to the pot before placing it in a sunny position. The children should water their seeds regularly and monitor the growth of the plants during the next few weeks, transplanting them when necessary to larger pots and to outside. A digital camera is ideal for recording growth. The children should monitor the plant growth with adult support.
2. As the children finish planting their seeds, ask an additional adult to help the children make a record of what they did.
3. A group could look at a collection of foods made with sunflowers (see Resources), and use these to make a frame for all the children's recordings of the activity.
 4. Fill the sand tray with slightly damp seed compost and a selection of pots, trowels and forks for the children to explore. This will give them experience of handling compost and of filling containers.
 5. Allow a group of four children to play in the 'potting shed' (role-play area), planting other seeds. Make sure they use seeds that have not been dressed with insecticide.

DIFFERENTIATION

Organise less able children into pairs, so that you can give them individual attention.

Invite more able children to plant their seeds in different places (for example, in an area of the school garden) and to monitor the growth to see whether the seeds grow better outdoors or indoors in pots. Allow them to record the growth, so that they have evidence on which to reach a conclusion.

ASSESSMENT

Group activity 2 can be used to assess the children's knowledge of how to plant seeds. Skilful questioning will allow you to find out which children know the conditions for growth, such as the need for water. If an adult helper supervises this activity, give him or her a prompt sheet with suitable questions.

PLENARY

Show the children the row of plant pots and explain the need to water the seeds every day. Talk about how much water each plant needs. Tell the children that they are going to watch how well the seeds grow over the next few weeks. You may wish them to count the days until the first sign of growth, or to record which seed grows first. Give the children a copy each of page 76 to use for recording the growth of their seeds.

OUTCOMES

● Know how to plant and care for seeds.
● Know that plants need water.
● Know that seeds grow into plants.

LINKS

Between units: this lesson links to Unit 3, Lesson 4.
Across the curriculum: the children develop their dexterity through handling and planting small seeds.

LESSON 15

OBJECTIVE

● To learn that different plants have different kinds of leaves.

RESOURCES

Main teaching activity: An umbrella plant, a Christmas pine; large sheets of paper (or a flip chart), a marker pen.
Group activities: 1. A laurel bush, holly bush, spider plant, cheese plant and yucca plant. (If it is autumn you can use a collection of leaves from the local area instead, and discuss colour as an attribute.) **2.** Paper, a pencil. **3.** Paints and wax crayons in suitable colours for leaves, a large picture of a tree, adhesive. **4.** Paper, pencils.

Vocabulary
shape, size, colour, straight, curved, edge, vein

PREPARATION

Choose three very different leaves and draw them on a sheet of A3 paper for Group activity 2.

INTRODUCTION

Place your umbrella plant and Christmas pine in the centre of the group, so that they can all see the leaves. Invite the children to gently feel the leaves on each plant. Make a note of their descriptions of how the leaves feel on each plant. Ask the children whether the leaves on the two plants are the same or different, and to describe the similarities and differences.

MAIN TEACHING ACTIVITY

Divide a large sheet of paper (or flip chart page) into two halves, with the headings 'The same' and 'Different' at the top. List all the things about the leaves that are the same (green, attached to branches, more than one leaf growing at each point) and the things that are different (one is sharp, the other is smooth; one is thin, the other is fat). If necessary, to help the children understand the process, repeat the activity with two more plants.

GROUP ACTIVITIES

1. With a group of children, look at the leaves on your plants (or the collection of leaves) closely and decide on a criterion for sorting. Sort the leaves into two types – for example, with spikes and without spikes; long and short; shiny and dull.

2. With another group, look closely at the leaves and talk about their features (such as veins, edges, top side and underside). Look at the three drawings one by one, and ask the children to describe the leaves. Encourage them to use their own words. Scribe the children's descriptions on each sheet of paper.

3. Ask the children to make prints (with paint) and wax crayon rubbings of the leaves using colours appropriate to the season, then cut them out and add them to a large picture of a tree with branches.

4. Ask the children to make close observational drawings of the leaves. Display these with the plants (or leaves) in a corner of the classroom.

DIFFERENTIATION

Ask more able children to choose a plant and write their own description of its leaves. Give them a word list to support their writing and prompt their ideas.

Work with less able children in small groups to explore the leaves, using the senses of touch and sight. Explore only one plant at a time, and focus on getting the children to draw or paint the leaves in the right colour.

ASSESSMENT

Collect the children's descriptions and drawings and keep them as evidence. On each one, note the child's contribution to Group activity 1 and whether he or she can sort the leaves according to given criteria.

PLENARY

Ask the children to say which is their favourite plant and why. *Is it because of the shape and colour of the leaves? Do they make the plant look pretty?*

OUTCOMES

● Know that leaves come in different sizes, shapes and colours.
● Know the features of leaves including veins, edges, top side and underside.

LINKS

Between units: this lesson links closely with all those that develop the observational skill of identifying similarities and differences. You may choose to select these lessons to develop this skill progressively.

LESSON 16

Objective	To learn that different plants can have different kinds of flowers.
Resources	Flowering pot plants and bunches of flowers (some of the same kind but with different-coloured flowers) including a lily; some non-protected wild flowers, including a dandelion and a daisy; paper, paints in various colours, scissors; a tree with blossom (or a picture of one); a collection of recycled materials, including drinking straws, garden canes and wires.
Main activity	Look at the flowers in your collection. Pass them around for the children to look at and handle. Ask them to look at the stem and describe what they see and feel. *Is the stem hard or soft? Can you squeeze it thinner? Is it thick or thin?* Explain that a stem is sometimes called a stalk. *What do you think the stem is used for?* If necessary, compare a plant stem to a drinking straw: *Water comes up through it.* 　　Look at all the flowers and ask the children to identify all the colours they can see. Look at one particular flower, such as a tulip or poppy, and look closely at the petals, stem and centre. *Is the flower all the same colour, or is the inside a different colour?* Sort the flowers according to their colour. *Are any colours not here?* (Brown, grey, black.) *Is one colour more common than the others?* Next, look closely at the petals. *What shape are the petals? Are they all the same size?* Investigate the number of petals on each flower. *Which flower has the most/least petals? Is there a number that is counted most often (for example, six)? Does the same kind of flower always have the same number and size of petals? Are all the petals in the same flower always the same colour?* (Yes.) 　　Organise Group activities with adult support: **1.** The children can paint large pictures of the flowers using bright colours, cut them out when dry and add them to a display. **2.** Look at a tree with blossom (or a picture of one). Explain that the trunk is the stem of the tree. Discuss the purposes of the trunk. Ask: *Does this tree have flowers? What do they look like?* Explain that the flowers on a tree are called 'blossom'. **3.** Ask the children to use recycled materials to make flowers and plants that match ones in your collection. For example, they could attach petal shapes to straws to make dandelions, or use garden canes for carnations. Talk with them about why they chose particular materials.
Differentiation	Ask less able children to draw their favourite flower and colour it correctly. Perhaps they could write, or ask an adult to scribe, a sentence describing the flower. More able children could choose two flowers to draw, and put circles around all the things that are different between them. If they are able, ask them to write a few sentences about how the two flowers are different.
Assessment	Keep the children's work (see Differentiation) as a record of their understanding. Note those children who know that a flower is made up of petals and an inside bit, and those who can recognise the stem.
Plenary	Look closely at a lily and talk about the petals and the inside bit. Show the children the pollen (take care not to make them sneeze). Discuss how bees collect the pollen and spread it from flower to flower, helping the plant to make seeds.
Outcomes	● Can recognise some features of a flower (even if they are unable to name them). ● Understand that flowers come in all shapes and sizes. ● Understand that different flowers have different numbers and shapes of petals. ● Learn that all the petals on the same flower have the same colour and shape. ● Can recognise things that are the same and things that are different.

LESSON 17

OBJECTIVE
● To learn that some plants are safe to eat and others are not.

Vocabulary

Names and colours of the fruits and vegetables in your collection; safe, unsafe, eaten, part, whole

RESOURCES

Main teaching activity: A collection of fruit and vegetables including a tomato, carrot, potato, lettuce and the fruits used in Unit 1, Lesson 1; sorting rings.
Group activities: 1 and 3. As above. **2.** Pictures of foods that are not safe to eat (such as toadstools and wild berries) and other fruits and vegetables (including sweetcorn, cabbage, cauliflower, peas and cucumber). **4.** Paints or crayons, paper.

PREPARATION

Take the children to visit the local supermarket or greengrocer's if there is one nearby. Look at the variety of fruit and vegetables that are being sold. Set up a 'greengrocer's shop' in the role-play area.

INTRODUCTION

Talk about the range of fruit and vegetables seen at the greengrocer's or supermarket. Ask the children which they do and do not like to eat. Explain that we all have different tastes and like to eat different things. All the things sold at the greengrocer's and supermarket are safe to eat (as long as they are fresh and have been washed). Other things can be found growing that are not safe to eat, such as toadstools (which look like ordinary mushrooms) and deadly nightshade berries (which look like blackcurrants). Tell the children that they should never eat anything unless an adult they know has said it is safe for them to do so.

MAIN TEACHING ACTIVITY

Show the children the fruits and vegetables in your collection. If the children are able to name any of these, encourage them to do so. If not, tell them the names. Ask them to sort the collection into sets of the same colour, so that they can see the range of colours more clearly. Now hold up each fruit or vegetable in turn and ask whether we eat all of it. Make two piles in sorting rings: those that we eat all of (such as a carrot) and those that we only eat part of (such as an orange).

GROUP ACTIVITIES

1. Ask an adult helper to repeat the Main teaching activity with groups of up to six children in order to reinforce the learning objective and make sure the children understand whether we eat all or part of each fruit and vegetable.
2. Show the children pictures of things that we should not eat and things that are safe to eat. Ask them to sort the pictures into two piles: things that are safe to eat and things that are not. Reinforce the idea that it is only safe to eat something if an adult we trust has said it is safe.
3. Allow groups of four children to 'buy' and 'sell' the fruit and vegetables in the 'greengrocer's shop' role-play area.
4. Ask the children to make pictures of fruit and vegetables to decorate the role-play area.

DIFFERENTIATION

With more able children, talk about which parts of fruits and vegetables we eat – for example, the seeds of pea plants, the leaves of cabbage plants and the seeds, flesh and peel of tomato plants. Ask them to identify, in turn, the vegetables and fruits of which we eat the seeds, leaves, flowers and roots. Ask them to record their choices in pictures.

Talk to less able children in groups of three or four about the more familiar vegetables. For example, ask them how they like their potatoes cooked. *Do you like baked potatoes, chips, roast potatoes, boiled potatoes? Do we ever eat the skin of the potato, or do we always take it off?*

ASSESSMENT

Ask the children to draw a picture of all the things in the collection that are safe to eat. More able children could label the items (fruit, vegetable) and their parts (seed, leaf and so on).

PLENARY

Use the children's pictures to make a class pictogram and so find out the class' favourite vegetable.

OUTCOMES

● Know that certain parts of a plant can be eaten.
● Know that not all plants can be eaten.

LINKS

Across the curriculum: this lesson can be linked to any healthy eating project that you have running in your school. Reinforce the children's awareness of the importance of a healthy diet.

LESSON 18

OBJECTIVES

● To learn that we need to eat in order to stay alive.
● To record information in the form of charts and graphs.

RESOURCES

Main teaching activity: A collection of vegetables (carrots, potatoes, cabbage, peas, broccoli, cauliflower and sweetcorn); pictures of these vegetables, a large blank chart; a copy of the song 'Paintbox' from *Harlequin* edited by David Gadsby and Beatrice Harrop (A&C Black).
Group activities: 1. As above. **2.** Plates, round-bladed knives. **3.** Paper plates, adhesive sticks, pictures of different foods. **4.** Paper, round-bladed knives, paint in various colours.

PREPARATION

Draw a chart on a large sheet of paper with one column for each vegetable in your collection. Cut out pictures of each of these vegetables, and make several photocopies that the children can colour and stick to the chart. Talk to the children as they play in the 'greengrocer's shop' role-play area for several days before you intend to carry out this lesson, so that you can find out all the vegetables that they do and do not like. Teach them the song 'Paintbox'.

INTRODUCTION

Sing the song 'Paintbox' with the children. Talk to them about what they usually eat for dinner. How many of them like to eat burgers, chips, vegetables? Explain that we need to eat in order to stay alive. Show the children the collection of vegetables and tell them that you are going to make a chart to show which vegetables they like to eat.

MAIN TEACHING ACTIVITY

Place one piece of each vegetable at the bottom of each column on the chart: a pea, a small carrot, a cabbage leaf, small pieces of broccoli and cauliflower and so on. Ask one of the children to say which vegetable he or she likes the best. Be prepared for someone to answer with a vegetable that is not part of your collection! If you have done your homework, this shouldn't happen (see Preparation). Invite the child to place the vegetable that he or she likes the best in the correct column. Ask the other children to help by explaining if necessary. Repeat the activity with a few other children.

GROUP ACTIVITIES

1. Repeat the activity with groups of six children, taking turns to place their favourite vegetable on a chart. When the chart is finished, ask them to replace each of the vegetables with a picture to represent it and stick their picture into place. Count how many pictures there are in each column, and invite the children to say which is their group's favourite vegetable.
2. Ask an adult to help the children cut up a selection of vegetables to enjoy at snack time. Carry out a risk assessment and check for allergies first. Talk about how eating certain vegetables is good for us and helps to keep us healthy.
 3. Give each child in a group a paper plate, an adhesive stick and pictures of food and vegetables. Ask the children to make a picture of the dinner they would like to have today. They can then take this home to show their parents or carers.
 4. Set up a printing table so that the children can print with potatoes and carrots. Talk about the shapes they have made (circles and ovals).

DIFFERENTIATION

Organise the more able children to do Group activity 1 together and include the choices of all the children in the class. As you remove the vegetable replace it with a cube of the same colour – for example orange for carrots, yellow for corn, light green for peas and so on. Transfer the information onto a block graph together and then invite the children to record the information individually on their own graph.

ASSESSMENT

During the Plenary session, note those children who are able to record their choices on the chart unaided. As you talk to the children during the activity, use focused questions to find out which children understand that we need to eat to stay alive.

Vocabulary

vegetables, carrots, sweetcorn, peas, potatoes, cabbage, cauliflower, broccoli, green, orange, white, brown, yellow, column, chart, graph, best, favourite

PLENARY

When all the groups have recorded their favourite vegetable choices onto separate charts, repeat the activity with all the children together. Ask each child in turn to choose a picture of his or her favourite vegetable and stick it in the correct column. When the chart is finished, count up how many there are in each column and invite the children to say which is the class' favourite vegetable. Write 'Our favourite vegetable' as a title and display the chart in the 'greengrocer's shop' role-play area.

OUTCOMES

● Know that we need to eat in order to stay alive.
● Know that eating certain vegetables is good for you.
● Know that information can be recorded in graphical form.

LINKS

Between units: this lesson links with several lessons in Unit 1.
Across the curriculum: the QCA *Design Technology Scheme of Work* has a Year 1 unit called 'Eat More Fruit and Vegetables', which could follow on from this lesson.

ASSESSMENT

LESSON 19

OBJECTIVES

● To assess the children's ability to name the parts of a flowering plant.
● To assess the children's ability to notice similarities and differences between plants, and to sort plants according to noticeable features.
● To assess the children's ability to record their findings by drawing pictures.

RESOURCES

Assessment activities: 1. A plant that has a stem, leaves and a flower; Post-it notes, a felt-tipped pen. **2.** Photocopiable page 77, scissors, adhesive sticks. **3.** Photocopiable page 78, pencils. **4.** Photocopiable page 79, scissors, adhesive, paper, pencils, sorting rings, labels.

ASSESSMENT ACTIVITY 1

Show the children the plant and ask them whether they can name any of the parts. Write their suggestions on Post-it notes and invite the child who made each suggestion to put the label on the correct part. Group the children according to ability for this activity, then set them off on the following Assessment activities.

ASSESSMENT ACTIVITY 2

Give the children a copy each of photocopiable page 77. Ask them to cut out the labels and stick them to the correct parts on the flower picture.

ASSESSMENT ACTIVITY 3

Give the children a copy each of photocopiable page 78. Ask them to ring the differences between the two plants.

ASSESSMENT ACTIVITY 4

Give the children a copy each of photocopiable page 79. Ask the children to cut out the pictures and sort them into sets:
● plants that have flowers and plants that do not;
● plants that have leaves and plants that do not;
● plants that have stems and plants that do not.

Assessment outcomes

On completion of the Assessment activities, you should know which children can:
● recognise and identify the flower, petals, stem, leaves and roots of a flowering plant
● know that plants need water to live.

PLENARY

Talk about the differences that the children have noticed between the two plants from Assessment activity 3. Make an enlarged copy of page 78 and complete this together.

How many legs?

	2	4	6	8
6				
5				
4				
3				
2				
1				

Number of animals

Number of legs

How many legs?

UNIT 2 ANIMALS & PLANTS

Name

Give me legs!

Name

Ant

Name

Beetle

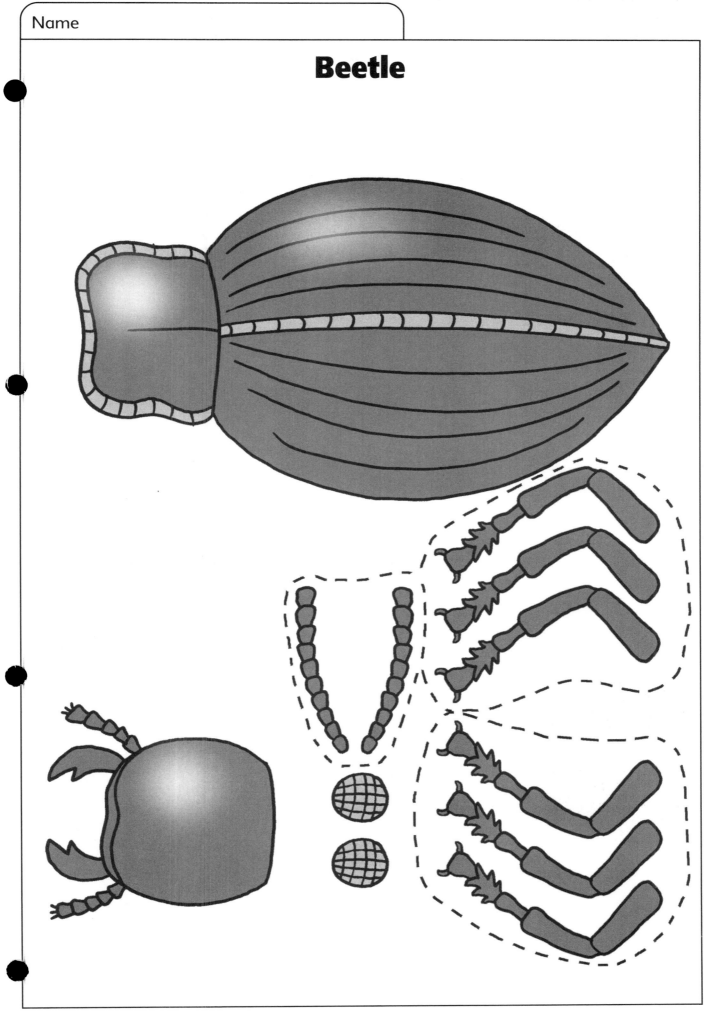

Ladybird

Name

Incey Wincey Spider

Draw the spider's web by joining the dots.

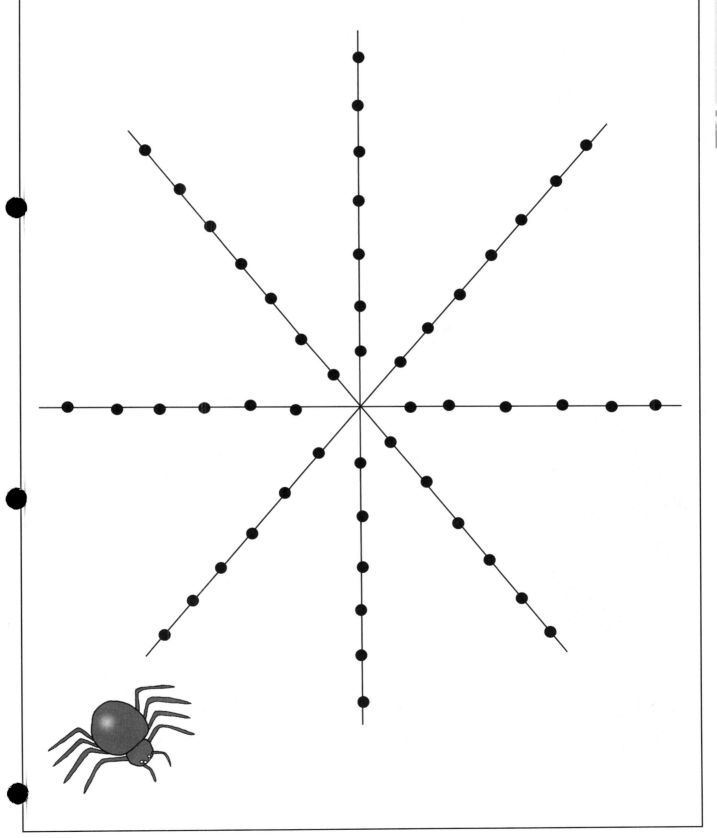

Name

See my sunflowers grow

Date:	Date:	Date:	Date:
The day I was planted	When I started to grow	Growing up	Fully grown

Parts of a plant

Match the words to the parts of the plant.

leaf

flower

stem

Name

Tell the difference

How are these pictures different? Draw (rings) around the things that are different.

Name

Cut out and sort

Out and about

ORGANISATION (12 LESSONS)

	OBJECTIVES	MAIN ACTIVITY	GROUP ACTIVITIES	PLENARY	OUTCOMES
LESSON 1	● To learn that there are many different features in the school environment. ● To learn that we have to live together with other people, plants and animals.	Talk about the ways that the school grounds are used.	Talk about how other people, plants and animals use the school grounds. Make a list of rules for using the school grounds. Make pictures of a favourite activity in the school grounds.	Look at the rules in the code of behaviour together.	● To recognise familiar places in their environment. ● To begin to think about the needs of other people, other living things and the environment.
LESSON 2	● To learn that many different kinds of animals live in, or visit, our school environment.	Talk about the places where you are likely to find animals in the school grounds.	Carry out an animal safari. Look closely at the animals found. Paint a picture of a chosen creature. Make a display of 'underground'.	Talk about the need for care of our living things in the environment.	● Learn to show concern for other living things. ● Begin to consider the feelings of other living things. ● Learn that animals should be left in their natural environment.
LESSON 3	● To learn that there are many different kinds of green plants.	Find and list all the kinds of plants in the school grounds.		Record the positions of the plants on a map of the school grounds.	● Can identify and recognise a range of green plants. ● Are learning to care for plants in their natural environment. ● Have begun to observe similarities and differences between plants. ● Can record their findings in pictorial form.
LESSON 4	● To learn that plants need to be looked after. ● To learn that plants need water to survive.	Plant and care for indoor plants.		Read *The Tiny Seed* by Eric Carle.	● Understand the need to water plants regularly. ● Can care independently for a number of different plants.
LESSON 5	● To learn that when it rains, we can prevent ourselves from getting wet. ● To learn that some materials are waterproof and so help to keep us dry.	Look at puddles and demonstrate how certain clothes and objects keep us dry when it rains.	Investigate waterproof materials. Test containers for leakage. Make wax-resist pictures. Make a display of clothes for rainy days.	Talk about the items in the display and how they are used to help keep us dry.	● Know that when it rains, we can get wet unless we protect ourselves from the rain. ● Know that rain is water that falls from the sky. ● Can recognise which materials are waterproof and begin to say why.
LESSON 6	● To talk about the weather in terms of whether it is sunny, raining, windy, cold or snowing.	Sing and talk about the different kinds of weather. Record the weather on a chart.		Count up the number of days on which it rained, was windy and so on. Total these on the chart.	● Know that there are many kinds of weather. ● Begin to describe the features of different kinds of weather. ● Begin to keep a simple record of the different kinds of weather.
LESSON 7	● To consider the different clothes that we wear at different times of the year.	Match clothing items to different kinds of weather.	Sort clothes according to weather. Add to a song about the weather. Select clothes for weather types. Make pictures of clothing for certain weather types.	Perform the song about the weather with the additional verses. Discuss the choice of collage materials.	● Know that we wear different kinds of clothing for different types of weather. ● Know that the clothing we wear in different weather is made from different materials. ● Know that people in different countries wear clothes that go with the main type of weather.

ORGANISATION (12 LESSONS)

	OBJECTIVES	MAIN ACTIVITY	GROUP ACTIVITIES	PLENARY	OUTCOMES
LESSON 8	● To learn that hats are worn for a variety of reasons, including protection from the weather.	Look at a variety of hats and talk about why they are worn.	Sort hats according to why they are worn. Note and explain the features of hats. Dress up in hats for role-play. Make a hat for a favourite toy. Make a collage of people wearing hats.	Talk about all the people who wear hats and say why they do so.	● Know that there are a variety of hats that are worn for different purposes. ● Recognise hats that are worn to protect us from the weather. ● Can identify similarities and differences between hats.
LESSON 9	● To consider the effects of the wind on our lives.	Use paper objects outdoors to explore the effects of the wind.		Look at windmills and talk about how they move in the wind.	● Know that the wind makes things move. ● Know that the wind helps to dry washing. ● Know that it is harder to run against the wind than with it.
LESSON 10	● To know that a variety of sounds can be heard in the local environment.	Collect sounds from the local environment. Explore how and why they and other sounds are made.		Explore the different sounds made with a drum.	● Know that a range of sounds can be heard in the local environment. ● Develop a range of vocabulary to describe the sounds they can hear. ● Know that we use our ears to hear.
LESSON 11	● To learn to keep their immediate surroundings tidy.	Learn to keep the classroom tidy. Discuss litter and recycling.		Talk about rubbish in the environment and safe behaviour.	● Know how to tidy up in the classroom. ● Know how to keep the parts of the school that they use clean. ● Know that they should never collect other people's rubbish.

	OBJECTIVES	MAIN ACTIVITY	ACTIVITIES 2 and 3	4 and 5	OUTCOMES
ASSESSMENT 12	● To assess the children's knowledge about the places where animals and plants live. ● To assess the children's ability to recognise different kinds of weather and clothes appropriate for them.	Say where various animals live.	Match animal pictures to the correct habitats. Match pictures of clothing to the correct weather types.	Dress a teddy for a windy, wet or sunny day. Make a list of rules about caring for the environment.	● Know that there are a variety of different weather types. ● Know that different kinds of clothing are worn for different types of weather. ● Know that different animals live in different habitats. ● Know that some animals are found in more than one habitat.

Context: CARING FOR OUR SCHOOL GROUNDS

The next three lessons are set within a topic on caring for our school grounds. Children's natural curiosity should be encouraged; however, it needs to be kept within some restrictions when they are dealing with living things. All three lessons emphasise this principle.

LESSON 1

OBJECTIVES
● To learn that there are many different features in the school environment that are used for different purposes by different people, animals and plants.
● To learn that we have to live together with other people, plants and animals.

RESOURCES

Main teaching activity: Enlarged photographs of different places in the school and its environment, such as the playground, field, hall, courtyard, car park and classroom.
Group activities: 1. Close-up photographs of specific features in and around the school, such as a hedgerow, tree, bush, pond, flowerbed and flowerpot; paper, pencils. **2.** A large sheet of paper, a marker pen. **3.** Paper, paints, coloured pencils or crayons.

Vocabulary
environment, live, co-operate, care, keep safe

PREPARATION

Take photographs of a number of places in the school and its environment, if possible using a digital camera so that you can zoom in and out on a computer to emphasise specific features of an area.

INTRODUCTION

Show the children each photograph, in turn, of the general areas in and around the school. Talk about the things that the children do in these areas: eat dinner, play football, plant flowers, play with friends, sit and talk, and so on.

MAIN TEACHING ACTIVITY

Show the area photographs again. Ask the children whether they think other people use these areas as well. Can they think of anything else that might live in these areas? Talk about the plants that can be seen in each picture, and ask the children what kinds of animal they think may be around somewhere. Emphasise that we are not the only people or the only animals that use these places, and that we have to think of others' needs as well as our own.

GROUP ACTIVITIES

1. Working with groups of six children, show them the close-up photographs (using the computer if possible) and talk about the other people, animals and plants that may also use this particular area of the school environment. Ask the children to draw pictures of all the animals and plants they can think of that might be found in the school environment.
2. Ask an adult helper to work with the children, making a list of rules for looking after the environment. The list should be written in positive terms – for example, instead of saying 'Do not pull the leaves off the trees', say 'Leave the leaves to live on the trees'.
3. Ask the children to paint and draw pictures of their favourite activity in the school grounds. These pictures can be displayed with the rules drawn up in Group activity 2 and the pictures drawn in Group activity 1.

DIFFERENTIATION

Give more able children appropriately levelled reference books or a CD-ROM to research the habitats of some of the animals and plants they thought of in Group activity 1.

With less able children, concentrate on either the plants or the animals in each habitat and spread the activities over a number of days.

ASSESSMENT

There are several things to note from this activity, including the children's understanding of where creatures live in the environment and the need to take care of it. These assessments can be followed up informally every time the children go into the environment to play and work. At the simplest level, it is important for the children to recognise that plants and animals are different and that they share a habitat.

PLENARY

Read out the rules that have been listed in Group activity 2. Display them on the display board with the children's pictures from Group activity 1.

OUTCOMES

- To recognise familiar places in their environment.
- To begin to think about the needs of other people, other living things and the environment.

LINKS

Across the curriculum: this lesson links well with personal and social development, since the children are asked to consider and show care for other people, for other living things and for the environment. Early geography skills are developed when the location of each of the habitats is discussed.

LESSON 2

OBJECTIVE

- To learn that many different kinds of animals live in, or visit, our school environment.

RESOURCES

Main teaching activity: A copy of the poem 'Hurt No Living Thing' by Christina Rossetti; books, posters and CD-ROMs with photographs of the animals you are likely to find.
Group activities: 1 and 2. Cardboard boxes, polythene sheeting, logs, grass cuttings, dead leaves, orange segments, sugar; paper, pencils, magnispectors. **3.** Paper, paints. **4.** A sponge, brown paint, green tissue paper, scissors, tights, newspaper.

Vocabulary

habitat, environment, hedge, tree trunk, leaf litter, group, single, lots, alone

PREPARATION

Carry out a survey of the school grounds to make sure that the children will be able to find many different kinds of animal. Look around the bases of trees, under hedges and leaf piles. A few days before the lesson, place logs, polythene sheeting, grass cuttings and leaf piles in a number of places in the school grounds. Leave a sugar trail and orange segments to attract ants, and wet cardboard boxes to attract slugs and snails. Make sure that you do not disturb any nesting birds. Organise an additional adult to accompany you. We recommend that you follow your school's policy for outdoor trips.

INTRODUCTION

Read out the poem 'Hurt No Living Thing'. Spend a few minutes talking about all the animals in the world, and how we need to treat them properly. Explain that the children are going to go outside to look for different kinds of animals that live and visit our school grounds.

MAIN TEACHING ACTIVITY

Talk about the kinds of places in the local environment where you might find animals. Show the children photographs of suitable animals from books and other sources; name the animals and briefly talk about their size, shape and colour. Direct the children's thinking towards the places where you have left items to attract the animals you want to find. Also talk about shrubs and bushes, where (depending on the time of the year) you might find caterpillars, butterflies, flies, greenflies and/or spiders. The school field will host a number of birds, and the trees surrounding the grounds (if you have them) may attract squirrels. Under the soil surface is the best place to find worms and centipedes.

Explain the rules about outdoor visits to the children, and make sure they know what to do when they see an animal: look, not touch; listen, not shout; tell an adult what they have found.

GROUP ACTIVITIES

1. Working with groups of six children, go into the environment to look at the different habitats. (An adult helper will be useful.) Explain that you have left certain items to attract the animals and that these are all environmentally friendly: they will not damage the places where the animals live (their 'habitats'). Make a list of all the animals that the children see. If possible, collect one animal of each type in a magnispector to take back into the classroom.

2. As the group returns, give each child in turn a magnispector containing a small animal. Let them examine the animals, under close adult supervision; then ask them to talk (to you and each other) about the animal. What do they notice about the colour, size, number of legs, how quickly it moves and so on? Pass the containers carefully around, so that the children can notice all of the things mentioned and possibly think of some more. Encourage the children to compare their specimens with the photographs used in the Main teaching activity. *Do they look the same?* At the end of each session, take the animals back and return them carefully to the place where they were found. Emphasise that you are doing this because we must look after living things and the places where they live.

3. Ask the children to choose one of the animals they have seen and paint a picture of it for a big display.

4. Make an 'underground' section for your display by sponge-painting in a variety of brown tones for mud and cutting out green triangle spears from tissue paper for the grass above it. Make worms and centipedes by stuffing tights with scrunched-up balls of newspaper and painting them with brown lines to show the segments, adding legs as appropriate.

DIFFERENTIATION

Give a more able group an opportunity to make close observational drawings of the creatures they bring back to the classroom. Use these to discuss the animals' features and habitats in more detail (as in Unit 2, Lessons 7 and 8). Ask the children whether the same animals were seen in a number of places, and whether these places had things in common. Were the animals found alone or in groups?

Talk to less able children about the names of the animals. Focus on their colour and size, repeating the objectives from Unit 2, Lessons 7 and 8.

ASSESSMENT

Listen as the children talk about the different animals they see. Make a mental note of the children's knowledge before the lesson and again at the end, so that you can assess new learning and progress. Note those children who are able to match the animal being observed to a picture in a book, on a poster or in a CD-ROM. Keep the more able children's drawings as evidence of their observational skills, and jot down briefly how they approached the task of observing and drawing the animals.

PLENARY

Read out the Christina Rossetti poem again, and talk about how the children cared for the animals they collected and observed. Ask one child (who you are sure will be able) to talk about how the animals were returned to the places where they were found, and the care that was taken to keep them safe.

OUTCOMES

- Learn to show concern for other living things.
- Begin to consider the feelings of other living things.
- Learn that animals should be left in their natural environment.

LINKS

Between units: Unit 2, Lessons 7 and 8 on observing insects and spiders.
Across the curriculum: this lesson links to personal and social development by raising the children's awareness of environmental issues.

LESSON 3

Objective	● To learn that there are many different kinds of green plants.
Resources	Paper, pencils, scissors, wax crayons; a large map of the local area, adhesive sticks; a local environment (which could be the school grounds or local garden centre) suitable for exploring a wide range and considerable number of green plants. Find a suitable place and make a list of all the green plants you can find. Make sure that it will be safe to look in this place. Check that none of your children has an allergy, especially hay fever or asthma. Organise additional adult help with the walk. Please follow your school's policy for outdoor visits, and any LEA policies on which plants to avoid.
Main activity	Explain to the children that they are going out to look for all the plants they can find. Talk about the places where plants might be found: gardens, shops, parks, the school field, alongside footpaths and so on. Talk briefly about what the children will see. (Depending on the time of year, they may see leaves and blossom on the trees; there may be daisies and dandelions on the ground.) Explain that they will have to look very closely, and that there may be an opportunity to find out what some of the plants feel like. However, they should ask first to make sure that touching the plant is safe both for them and for the plant. Emphasise that it is never safe to taste a wild plant, and that this is forbidden. Take the children out and make a note of all the plants you find. Include grasses, trees, hedgerows, mosses, flowers, vegetables, shrubs, fruits and their cases, seeds, pot plants and wild flowers. You may need to get down on your hands and knees to look in the grass for some mosses. Other plants can be found around and under hedgerows. Ask the children to draw pictures of some of the plants they see. Cut these out if you have time. The children can make wax crayon rubbings of the different tree trunks, and compare the patterns at a later date.
Differentiation	Talk to more able children about the different species of flowers and trees. On returning to the classroom, ask them to make a chart showing the different kinds of flowers, trees and plants they have found. Put the less able children with an adult helper who can check whether they are able to identify the range of plants in the local environment. If necessary, the helper should tell them the names of four plants, then encourage them to draw these and write their names for future reference.
Assessment	Listen to the children's conversations during the Main activity and use focused questions to assess their knowledge and understanding of plants. Use the children's recordings to gain further assessment information. Note those children who can recognise a plant – some may not be able to at the start of the lesson.
Plenary	Record the children's findings on a large map of the local area, showing where they found the different plants. Allow the children to stick their pictures to the right places on the map. Talk about the colour, size and texture of some of the plants the children have found.
Outcomes	● Can identify and recognise a range of green plants including trees, shrubs, flowers, grasses and mosses. ● Are learning to care for plants in their natural environment. ● Have begun to observe similarities and differences between different plants. ● Can record their findings in pictorial form.

LESSON 4

Objectives	● To learn that plants need to be looked after. ● To learn that plants need water to survive.
Resources	Bulb fibre, seed compost, bulbs (one for each child), a large plastic tub (such as a 2 litre ice cream tub), a collection of indoor and outdoor plants, a packet of birdseed, water, black sugar paper, a dark place, a sand tray; paper, pencils; *The Tiny Seed* by Eric Carle (Picture Puffin). Gather a range of plants to keep in the classroom, or identify some that need regular watering outside. These could be the sunflowers planted previously, other flowers and shrubs in your garden area, or plants in window-boxes and hanging baskets.
Main activity	Organise a number of Group activities with adult help: **1.** Show the children the indoor plants in your collection, find a place for them to live and organise a rota for watering them on a regular basis (this will depend on the kinds of plants you have). Show the children the outdoor plants you have, and explain that these will need watering when there has been no rain for a number of days. **2.** Together, plant the birdseed in a tray on a bed of seed compost. Water the seeds and put them on a windowsill to germinate. Check the compost daily to make sure that it does not dry out; water it appropriately. **3.** Ask groups of six children to mix the bulb fibre with water until it feels damp. Allow every child to feel the damp mixture. The children should plant the bulbs in a large plastic tub (October is the best time for this) and cover them with black sugar paper before placing the tub in a dark place. They should check the bulb fibre every week and make sure that it is still damp. Ask an adult helper to work with each group when the planting is finished, encouraging them to record in pictures or words what they did. **4.** Allow the children to explore the texture of seed compost and bulb fibre in the sand tray. Check first that the fibre is safe: free from small creatures and sharp pieces.
Differentiation	Talk to more able children about whether compost is needed for the bulbs to grow. Plant one bulb in a special container (see diagram) that allows the roots to reach water, and compare the growth of this bulb with the others. Allow the children to plant some bulbs outside and record when they start to grow. Talk about why the bulbs grow much faster inside than outside (because there is more light and warmth), and relate the discussion to the conditions of growth (plants need light, warmth and water to grow). Repeat Group activity 3 with less able children a few weeks later to reinforce the learning.

starts to shoot

bulb sits on top

roots grow down into water

water nearly to top

clear plastic container

Assessment	Note those children who remember to water the plants and bulbs.
Plenary	Read *The Tiny Seed* by Eric Carle (Picture Puffin).
Outcomes	● Understand the need to water plants regularly. ● Can care independently for a number of different plants.

Context: THE WEATHER

The next five lessons give the children the opportunity to consider the impact that the weather has on their lives, and the need to protect themselves from elements such as sunlight, rain, cold and wind. The lessons focus on how appropriate clothing changes with the seasons in order to protect us from the weather.

LESSON 5

OBJECTIVES

● To learn that when it rains, we can prevent ourselves from getting wet.
● To learn that some materials are waterproof and so help to keep us dry, but others are not.

RESOURCES

Main teaching activity: Wellington boots, an umbrella, a large sheet of plastic, an empty bowl, a watering can, water, a metal tray.
Group activities: 1. A watering can, water, a range of materials (some waterproof, some not), a teddy bear, adhesive tape, adhesive sticks, scissors. **2.** A water tray, a range of containers (some waterproof, some not). **3.** Wax crayons, paper, colourwash (thinly mixed paint). **4.** An old raincoat, rain hat, cagoule, umbrella and pair of Wellington boots; books about rainy weather.

Vocabulary

waterproof, wet, dry, sprinkle, splash, splosh, splish, pitter, patter

PREPARATION

Mix several pots of colourwash in a range of colours. You may choose to do this activity on a rainy day, when the children are able to go outside and splash in puddles; or following a dance lesson, when the children pretend to splash, stamp and jump in and out of puddles. Cover the floor with plastic sheeting.

INTRODUCTION

Show the children the Wellington boots and ask them when they would wear these. Invite one of the children to say why the boots are worn on rainy days. Next, show the children the raincoat. Pass it around, so that they can feel the material from which it is made. Ask them to describe the material, encouraging them to use words such as 'waterproof'.

MAIN TEACHING ACTIVITY

Gather the children around you in a circle. Place the metal tray in the centre of the circle on the plastic sheeting. Sprinkle water from the watering can, held at a height so that when the water hits the metal tray it makes a pitter-patter sound. Talk about the sound the water makes and compare it to rain. Point out how a puddle forms on the tray. Empty the tray into a bowl. Ask the children whether they can think of a way to stop the tray from getting wet. After you have listened to their suggestions, invite a child to stand on the tray and pretend to pour water over his or her head. When the squeals have died down, ask the children how you can keep the volunteer (victim) dry. Put the umbrella up at this point, and pour water from the watering can over the umbrella so that it runs down and onto the plastic sheeting. (Don't pour too much water!) Explain that the umbrella is made from a special material that stops the water going through it and prevents people getting wet. The material is 'waterproof'.

GROUP ACTIVITIES

1. Work with groups of four children to investigate a range of waterproof and non-waterproof materials and sort them into two sets. Use the materials to make a suitable raincoat for a teddy bear.
2. Allow a group of children to work unaided with a water tray, using a range of containers: some that are waterproof, some that are not. Challenge the children to find the containers that leak or do not hold water.
3. Ask an adult helper to work with groups of four children, drawing pictures with wax crayons. As the children finish, the helper should help them to paint over the pictures with a thin colourwash and talk about how the wax comes through because it resists the water. He or she should explain that wax is waterproof: it resists water and doesn't get wet.
4. Together, make a display of clothing that is worn on rainy days.

DIFFERENTIATION

With more able children, look at the shapes of umbrellas and rain hats and talk about their design. Point out how they spread out over the top of a person to take the water away from the body.

Talk to less able children as they play in the water about the containers that leak and the ones that do not. Once they have understood this basic idea, lead them to the concept of waterproof and non-waterproof materials.

ASSESSMENT

Note which children are able to sort the materials into 'waterproof' and 'non-waterproof' and which can make a waterproof coat for a teddy bear, choosing from a range of materials. Note which children are able to select materials that are waterproof, thus showing an understanding of this property.

PLENARY

Talk about the display you have made of clothing that is worn on wet days. Emphasise that these items are made from waterproof materials, and that we wear them to keep ourselves warm and dry. Invite the children to bring items into school to add to the display.

OUTCOMES

● Know that when it rains, we can get wet unless we protect ourselves from the rain.
● Know that rain is water that falls from the sky.
● Can recognise which materials are waterproof and begin to say why.

LINKS

Between units: this lesson links with Unit 4, Lesson 4 on bubbles.

LESSON 6

Objective	● To talk about the weather in terms of whether it is sunny, raining, windy, cold or snowing.	
Resources	Pictures of different kinds of weather; labels with the names of types of weather; a chart on which to glue pictures (see illustration); a copy of 'The Weather Song' from *Spring Tinderbox* (A&C Black). You may wish to use children's pictures from an earlier lesson, or those from photocopiable page 95.	
Main activity	Sing 'The Weather Song', or a similar song. Talk to the children about the weather you have had recently. Encourage them to talk about whether the weather is sunny, frosty, foggy, rainy/wet, snowy, windy or cloudy. Describe the features of each type of weather – for example, on foggy days it is difficult to see, it is wet and cold; on rainy days we need to wear special clothes or carry umbrellas to help us keep dry. Every day, talk about the kind of weather we are having and stick a suitable picture and label onto the space on the chart. Depending on your group and the time of year, you may wish to keep a weekly or monthly chart to discuss at the end of each week or month. You may also wish to record the weather two or three times during the day, if it is changeable enough to make this worthwhile. This in itself is an important learning outcome, as the children need to realise that the weather can change quickly.	
Differentiation	Talk to more able children about shadows, and how these are clearer on sunny days. Challenge them to find shadows of objects and themselves when they go out to play. Analyse the weather statistics with this group of children at the end of the month, and transfer the information on to a block graph. Ask less able children to draw a picture of their favourite type of weather, giving reasons for their choice. An adult helper can record their reasons for them.	
Assessment	After a few weeks (depending on the children's ability), give each child a blank chart and ask them to record the different kinds of weather throughout the next week. They should work individually. Keep the records as evidence of the children's attainment.	
Plenary	At the end of each week or month, count the number of sunny days, foggy days, rainy days and so on. Write each total at the end of the row or column for that kind of weather.	
Outcomes	● Know that there are many kinds of weather. ● Begin to describe the features of different kinds of weather. ● Begin to keep a simple record of the different kinds of weather.	

LESSON 7

OBJECTIVE

● To consider the different clothes that we wear at different times of the year.

RESOURCES

Main teaching activity: A range of clothes for all types of weather; a copy of 'The Weather Song' from *Spring Tinderbox* (A&C Black).
Group activities: 1. Paper, pencils. **3.** Dressing-up clothes for all types of weather. **4.** Large sheets of paper, crayons, a range of collage materials. You will need picture reference books for the extension activity.

Vocabulary

hot, sunny, wet, frosty, snowy, hail, cold

INTRODUCTION

Sing 'The Weather Song' and talk about sunny, windy and rainy weather. Remind the children of other kinds of weather discussed in Lesson 6.

MAIN TEACHING ACTIVITY

Invite the children to choose one of the types of weather and to find items of clothing that we are likely to wear in this weather. Talk about the type of material, its thickness, its texture and so on. Repeat the activity for other types of weather.

GROUP ACTIVITIES

1. Work with a group of six children, sorting the clothes into sets to wear on rainy, snowy, frosty, warm or sunny days. Ask the children to say which items of clothing can be worn for more than one type of weather (for example, a woolly hat for snowy and frosty weather). They can record their ideas by drawing pictures of the items, with the type of weather as a title.
2. Ask an adult helper to work with a group of children, making up additional verses for 'The Weather Song'. These could include verses on frost, snow and hail. The children could add body percussion to each verse.
3. Organise a dressing-up race for six children. Give each child a type of weather. When you say 'Go', the children have to get dressed appropriately. The first child to be dressed in the correct set of clothes is the winner.
4. Draw around three children. Together, use these to make large collage pictures of children wearing suitable clothes for wet, cold and sunny weather.

DIFFERENTIATION

Take less able children outside every day and talk about whether they need a coat, a raincoat or a sunhat. Discuss why this is, and relate it to the weather on that day.

Invite more able children to use books to research the clothes worn in other countries, for example a very hot or a very cold country. Talk about the differences and similarities between the clothes for these two extremes of weather.

ASSESSMENT

Watch the children during Group activity 3, and note those who are able to choose the correct clothing for their designated weather type.

PLENARY

Ask the groups composing additional verses to the song to perform their compositions dressed in appropriate clothing. Talk about the clothes that the children in the large pictures are dressed in. Ask the children what kind of collage materials they chose for each item (for example, wool for a jumper, plastic for a raincoat).

OUTCOMES

● Know that we wear different kinds of clothing for different types of weather.
● Know that the clothing we wear in different weather is made from different materials.
● Know that people in different countries wear clothes that go with the main type of weather (for example, to keep cool or warm).

LINKS

Across the curriculum: many stories and poems about the weather can be used as texts for literacy lessons and as starting points for writing and drama. There are also opportunities to talk about the different kinds of cultural dress in order to develop the children's awareness and acceptance of other cultures.

LESSON 8

OBJECTIVE

● To learn that hats are worn for a variety of reasons, including protection from the weather.

RESOURCES

Main teaching activity: A range of (real and/or toy) hats such as a sun hat, police officer's helmet, crash helmet, builder's helmet, horse-rider's hat, bobble hat and rain hat; a copy of 'My Hat It Has Three Corners' from *Okki-Tokki-Unga* edited by Beatrice Harrop (A&C Black).
Group activities: 1. Photocopiable page 96, scissors, sorting rings, paper, glue. **2.** Paper, a pen. **3.** Several clothing items and hats for the children to dress up in; a digital camera. **4.** Materials for making small toy hats (such as paper, plastic sheeting, tin foil, card and empty yoghurt pots). **5.** Magazines with pictures of people who wear hats, scissors, adhesive sticks, paper.

PREPARATION

Ask the children's parents or carers whether they have any hats at home that you could borrow for this lesson. Photocopy page 96 onto card and cut out the pictures.

Vocabulary
hat, helmet, weather, protect, hard, waterproof

INTRODUCTION

Sing the song 'My Hat It Has Three Corners'. Show the children one of the hats in your collection and make up other verses about this hat: it has no corners, it has a feather, it has a brim and so on.

MAIN TEACHING ACTIVITY

Pass a toy police helmet (if you have one) around the group and ask the children each to say one thing about it. Prompt them to say whether it is hard or soft; big or small; square, round or flat. Can they tell you why this helmet is hard, tall and round? Explain that it is made to protect the police officer's head. Find all the other hats that are used to protect peoples' heads from injury, and put them to one side. Look at the other hats left in your collection. Ask the children to describe the features of this group of hats. When they have finished, put these hats together and ask the children to say what they are all used for. If necessary, tell them that all the hats in this group are used to protect us from the weather. Explain that they are going to explore these hats during the Group activities.

GROUP ACTIVITIES

1. Work with a group of six children to sort the pictures of hats from a copy of page 96 into sets, according to whether they are worn to protect us from the weather or from other things. Glue the pictures into the appropriate sets on paper as a simple record of the children's decisions.
2. Ask an adult helper to work with groups of four children to explore the features of each type of hat. They should talk about specific features (the peak on a sun cap, the brim on a sombrero, the hardness of a crash helmet and so on), trying to explain them. Ask the helper to note down the children's ideas.
3. Put a variety of hats and dressing-up clothes in an area of the classroom and allow the children to dress up and act as various characters. Use a digital camera to record them.
4. Give the children a variety of materials and ask them to make a sun hat for their favourite doll or teddy, or a helmet for their Action Man.
5. Give the children magazines and ask them to cut out all the pictures of people who are wearing hats, stick them onto paper and add a sentence about each one before making the pages into a book.

DIFFERENTIATION

During Group activity 2, give more able children two different hats (very different or quite similar, depending on their ability). With the children, make a list of all the things that are the same about the two hats and all the things that are different.
  Give less able children time to draw a picture of their favourite hat and to say who would wear it and why.

ASSESSMENT

Use Group activity 1 to assess the children's understanding of why we wear certain hats. Question them about the materials from which each hat is made and the hat's suitability for its purpose.

PLENARY

Ask the group who cut pictures from magazines to talk about what they found and the types of hats the people were wearing. Reinforce the idea that we sometimes wear hats to protect us from the weather.

OUTCOMES

● Know that there are a variety of hats that are worn for different purposes.
● Recognise hats that are worn to protect us from the weather.
● Can identify similarities and differences between hats, according to their materials and features.

LINKS

Between units: this lesson relates to work in Unit 4 on materials and their properties.
Across the curriculum: this lesson can be taught within a topic about 'People Who Help Us', and can be related to work on any people who wear uniforms. It also provides a good context for the development of imaginative play.

LESSON 9

Objective	● To consider the effects of the wind on our lives.
Resources	A 'windy day' story, such as *A Windy Day* by Elspeth Graham (OUP) or *Mrs Mopple's Washing Line* by Anita Hewett (Red Fox); strips of paper (one per child) 10cm wide and 1m long; a fan (optional); sheets of A1 card; paper and art materials for making a frieze; a set of doll's clothes, pegs, string; thin card or plastic sheeting, dowelling, pins, beads, scissors, adhesive. For extension: materials to make sailboats, a water tray. For support: kites.
Main activity	If possible, take the children outside on a windy day. Read your chosen story to the children and talk about the effects of the wind. Give each child a strip of paper. Ask the children to hold it out in one hand and see what the paper does. *Does it move or does it stay still?* Repeat the activity outside on a windy day, or use a fan to create a wind. Watch the shapes made by the paper. *Does the paper hang down or does it move about?* On returning to the classroom, talk about the movement of the paper and ask the children to make simple drawings of what happened. Organise a number of Group activities with adult help: **1.** Go outside on a windy day with sheets of A1 card and try to run against the wind. **2.** Make a 'windy day frieze' in the classroom and add words to describe movement. **3.** Wash a doll's clothes and peg them on a string 'washing line' outdoors to dry. **4.** Make windmills from thin card or plastic sheeting (see diagram overleaf). As the sails spin in the wind (or as the children blow them), talk about the way they move.
Differentiation	Explore the push of the wind with more able children by making light sailboats to blow along in the water tray (see diagram below). With less able children, play outside with kites on windy days (first make sure that there are no overhead cables); encourage them to observe the effects of the wind on the kites' movement, and talk about the way the kites move.
Assessment	Note those children who are able to talk about the effects of the wind as they contribute to the frieze. Note those who are unable to make suggestions; take them out on other windy days to observe effects such as leaves moving and hair blowing in their eyes.
Plenary	Ask the group who made the windmills to talk about how these move when blown by the wind. Watch as they spin faster when someone blows harder. Leave them outside, stuck firmly in the ground, on a windy day and watch them as they spin.
Outcomes	● Know that the wind makes things move. ● Know that the wind helps to dry washing. ● Know that it is harder to run against the wind than with it.

card or paper
stiff straw
polystyrene tray

LESSON 10

Objective	● To know that a variety of sounds can be heard in the local environment.
Resources	A portable (battery-operated) cassette recorder or Dictaphone; paper, pencils; a drum, objects for making sounds on a drum (see below); a commercial audio tape of everyday sounds (available from early learning centres).
Main activity	Take the children out a few days before on a 'sound walk' and listen to the sounds all around. Make a recording of these using a portable tape recorder or Dictaphone. Remind the children of all the sounds they heard on the sound walk. Ask whether anyone knows which part of the body we use to hear with. (Our ears.) Play the tape from the walk, stopping it after each sound and asking the children what they think is making the sound. Talk about the types of sound the items make: a squeaking sound, a loud sound, a quiet, soft, whistling, grating sound and so on. Organise a number of Group activities with adult help: **1.** Work with an adult helper to draw pictures of things that make high, loud, quiet, whistling, whispering and/or squeaking sounds. **2.** Explore the different sounds that can be produced on a drum, using a variety of objects such as a nailbrush, rice and erasers as well as a range of beaters. **3.** Draw pictures of things that make a sound as a message, such as a doorbell, a telephone or an ambulance siren. **4.** Small groups can play the 'recognising sounds' game (as above) with a commercially bought tape of sounds. Encourage them to operate the tape recorder independently in order to develop their early ICT skills.
Differentiation	Help less able children to explore the sounds made by everyday objects such as a squeaky door, hammering wooden blocks and a doorbell. After they have listened to each sound, ask them to point to the object that makes the squeaking, ringing or banging sound. This will also help them to develop the vocabulary needed to describe a range of sounds heard in the environment. More able children could investigate how far away the sounds made by a range of everyday objects (such as a ticking clock, a dripping tap and a telephone) can be heard.
Assessment	Play the sound walk tape to the children again, asking them to draw pictures of the things they can hear. To make this easier for less able children, provide worksheets containing suitable pictures for them to colour and tell them which colour to use for each sound (so that you can keep track of their responses).
Plenary	Ask the children exploring the drum to explain the range of sounds they can make. If you wish, find a suitable poem and use drum sounds to accompany it (depicting the sounds of rain, thunder and so on).
Outcomes	● Know that a range of sounds can be heard in the local environment. ● Develop a range of vocabulary to describe the sounds they can hear. ● Know that we use our ears to hear.

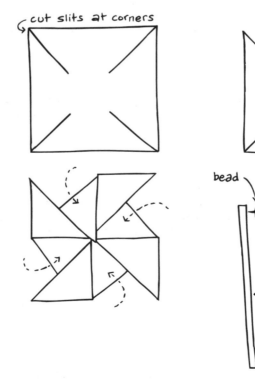

cut slits at corners

fold into centre

bead   bead

pin

←paper

←stick

Pin through centre of windmill (holding folded corners in the middle).

LESSON 11

Objective	● To learn to keep their immediate surroundings tidy.
Resources	A camera, a friendly cleaner; large sheets of paper, a marker pen, paints; examples of objects that can be recycled.
Main activity	Organise a particularly messy activity, such as cutting and pasting, and give the children very little time to tidy up! Take a photograph of the classroom at the end of the day, and another (with his or her permission) of the cleaner tidying up. Show the children the photograph and ask them whether they know where this photograph was taken. Do they know who cleaned the mess up? Show them the photograph of the cleaner.
	Talk to the children about all the classroom activities they do that leave a mess. Make a list of these activities. Separate out the ones that involve leaving litter for others to clear up, such as spilling sand, water or paint. Ask the children how they could make the cleaner's job easier. What can they do to keep their classroom tidy? Together, make a list of rules for keeping the classroom tidy. Make the rules positive, and include directions on how to follow the rules. Include rules such as: 'Put all the rubbish in the bin'; 'Tidy your own place'; 'Hang your coat on your peg, don't leave it on the floor'. Ask the children to make 'Keep Our School Litter-Free' posters, and to design litter bins that would be fun to use. They can paint big pictures of these designs for display with the posters.
	Make a collection of objects that can be recycled, and find out where the nearest recycling centre is. Many are adjacent to supermarkets. Write to parents and carers, asking them to point these out to the children on their next visit (perhaps taking newspapers, glass bottles or cans to be recycled).
	After a busy day cutting and sticking, challenge the children to pick up all the litter. Explain that it is safe to do so because it is *their* rubbish and they know how it was made! Do a litter patrol when the children have finished, and count the bits of litter still left on the floor. Emphasise that the children should never pick up other people's litter: only adults should do this task, as the litter may be dangerous.
Differentiation	This lesson is a good opportunity to establish routines: what to use to sweep up the sand, wipe over the table, collect big pieces of litter and so on. Carry out a risk assessment with more able children to encourage them to spot these things for themselves and to tidy things away independently.
Assessment	This is a good opportunity to find out what types of litter the children are already aware of, including unsocial and unwelcome items. It is important that they know what to do if they find things that they think they should not touch because of health risks: tell an adult immediately.
Plenary	Emphasise the idea that there are signs of people everywhere: some things that are nice and others that are not so nice. Reinforce the message that the children should never touch or pick up litter themselves, but that it is important that they (as individuals) use a litter bin or take their own litter home.
Outcomes	● Know how to tidy up in the classroom. ● Know how to keep the parts of the school that they use clean. ● Know that they should never collect other people's rubbish.

ASSESSMENT

LESSON 12

OBJECTIVES
● To assess the children's knowledge about the places where animals and plants live.
● To assess the children's ability to recognise different kinds of weather and clothes appropriate for them.

RESOURCES

Main activity: A set of models or pictures of various animals, including some that live in water, on land and underground; blue, green and brown sheets of paper.
Assessment activities: 2. Photocopiable pages 97 and 98, scissors, adhesive sticks.
3. Photocopiable page 99, pencils. **4.** A teddy bear; sets of small clothes for wet, cold and sunny weather. **5.** Paper, pencils.

PREPARATION

Make enlarged copies of photocopiable pages 97 and 98. Make enough copies of photocopiable page 99.

INTRODUCTION

Show the children the models or pictures of animals in your collection. Ask them to identify and name each one.

MAIN ASSESSMENT ACTIVITY

Talk about the animals in your collection and ask the children where they live. *Do they live on land, in water or under the ground?* With more able children, you may wish to sort the animals further into groups such as those who live in a hedgerow, in the desert, in the sea, in a pond or on a farm. Ask the children, one at a time, to choose an animal and place it on a sheet of coloured paper to show where the animal lives for most of the time: green for on land, blue for in water or brown for underground. An adult helper will be useful to record the children's discussions during this activity as they make decisions about animals such as frogs, birds and worms.

ASSESSMENT ACTIVITY 2

Ask the children to cut out the animal pictures on page 97 and place them in the appropriate habitat on page 98. Check their decisions, then stick the pictures in place. (If necessary, explain that the word 'habitat' means where an animal lives in the environment.)

ASSESSMENT ACTIVITY 3

Ask the children to match each item of clothing to the correct weather picture on page 99 by drawing lines.

ASSESSMENT ACTIVITY 4

Ask the children to select items from a range of clothing in order to dress the teddy bear for a windy, wet or sunny day.

ASSESSMENT ACTIVITY 5

Ask an adult helper to work with the children, making a list of rules for caring for the environment.

PLENARY

Talk about the dressed teddies, asking the children to say what kind of weather each one is dressed for. Ask: *How do you know?* Link their answers to the pictures on page 99, which you may wish to complete with the children at the same time.

ASSESSMENT OUTCOMES

On completion of these Assessment activities, you should know which children have attained the following objectives linked to knowledge and understanding of the world:
- Know that there are a variety of different weather types.
- Know that different kinds of clothing are worn for different types of weather.
- Know that different animals live in different habitats.
- Know that some animals are found in more than one habitat.

Name

Clothes for the weather

Exploring materials

ORGANISATION (12 LESSONS)

	OBJECTIVES	MAIN ACTIVITY	GROUP ACTIVITIES	PLENARY	OUTCOMES
LESSON 1	● To develop the vocabulary, particularly of texture, associated with a range of objects made from a variety of materials.	Play 'texture dominoes' with objects.	Sort items with different textures. Make wax rubbings of wallpaper. Display textures of a given type. Role-play a hardware store.	Talk about the textures recorded by the wax rubbings.	● Can use pictures to record what they have done. ● Can use simple language to describe texture. ● Can use their sense of touch to explore items found in the home.
LESSON 2	● To use the senses to explore, sort and identify the materials from which various objects are made.	Sort and match materials by appearance, texture and magnetic properties.		Make a wall of different textures for the children to explore.	● Know that there are many different materials. ● Know that different materials have different textures and look different. ● Can sort familiar materials by name.
LESSON 3	● To recognise common materials and learn their names: wood, paper, fabric, metal.	Compare different kinds of paper. Make a display of paper items.	Make displays of fabrics, metal and wood. Play an 'Odd material out' game. Make paper decorations, fans and wrappers. Sort objects by material.	Add items to the displays according to the material from which they are made.	● Can recognise paper, fabric, metal and wood. ● Can sort materials into named groups. ● Can begin to describe the properties of wood, metal, fabric and paper.
LESSON 4	● To learn that soap and water mixed together make bubbles.	Make bubble mixture and blow bubbles.	Make bubbles from different soapy materials. Make bubble sculptures. Draw bubbles. Make bubble paint patterns.	Look at the bubble patterns together and talk about what you can see.	● Know that soap mixes with water. ● Know that mixing soap and water together makes bubbles. ● Are able to co-operate, work together, share and take turns.
LESSON 5	● To investigate what happens when we try to mix oil and water. ● To learn that not all liquids mix with water.	Make oil pattern pictures. Explore how different types of oil behave in water.		Talk about the effects of oil on clothes and birds' feathers.	● Know that oil and water do not mix. ● Know that oils can have different colours, and some oils are thicker than others. ● Know that oil floats on water.
LESSON 6	● To learn that the thicker a mixture is, the harder it is to stir. ● To learn that the more water is added, the runnier a mixture becomes.	Explore how the thickness of a cornflour mixture affects how easy it is to stir and pour.	Order mixtures by how easy they are to stir. Make cornflour finger paintings. Stir and blend a range of liquids. Make dripping paint pictures.	Make a collection of liquids. Talk about what a liquid is.	● Know that a mixture can be thin (runny) or thick (stiff). ● Can compare the thickness of two mixtures, and order mixtures by how thick or thin they are. ● Recognise some of the physical properties of liquids.
LESSON 7	● To learn that sand, when mixed with the right amount of water, will stick together. ● To learn that dry sand does not stick together. ● To learn that damp or wet sand is made by mixing dry sand with water.	Make damp sand. Build sandcastles to explore its properties.		Talk about the different sandcastles made by the children.	● Know that damp sand sticks together. ● Know that you mix dry sand and water to make damp sand. ● Know the similarities and differences between dry and damp sand. ● Can describe what damp sand feels like.

ORGANISATION (12 LESSONS)

	OBJECTIVES	MAIN ACTIVITY	GROUP ACTIVITIES	PLENARY	OUTCOMES
LESSON 8	● To learn that the shape of a mixture can be changed by rolling.	Make dough for biscuits or pastry.	Make biscuits or pastry in groups. Flatten and roll out play dough. Role-play a baker's shop.	Enjoy the products and review the process.	● Know that squashing and rolling-out change the shape of dough. ● Know that dry ingredients will mix together. ● Know that dry ingredients will stick together when mixed with a liquid.
LESSON 9	● To learn that the shape of materials can be changed by squashing, pulling and bending.	Make pizza bases. Prepare toppings.		Put toppings onto pizza bases and cook.	● Know that the shape of dough can be changed by squashing, rolling and coiling round.
LESSON 10	● To learn that some dry ingredients will mix with water and that when you add more water, the mixture becomes runnier.	Make batches of cakes. Make and colour icing. Ice the cakes.		Sort dry ingredients into those that will and will not mix with water.	● Know that icing sugar will mix with water. ● Know that when water mixes with a dry ingredient, the mixture is wet. ● Know that a cake mixture changes when cooked. ● Know that the colour of icing changes when food colouring is added.
LESSON 11	● To learn that the texture of a mixture can be changed by cooking.	Make porridge. Talk about the changes caused by mixing and cooking.	Taste toppings on the porridge. Make oat biscuits. Lay the table for the three bears. Order the steps in the process of making porridge. List foods that change when cooked.	Make a chart of the children's favourite toppings.	● Know that the way porridge looks changes when it is cooked. ● Know that porridge has a different texture when cooked. ● Know that heat is used to cook things. ● Know that we should never touch hot things, as they can burn us.
	OBJECTIVES	MAIN ACTIVITY	ACTIVITIES 2 and 3	4 and 5	OUTCOMES
ASSESSMENT 12	● To find out what the children know about changing the shape of materials.	Explain what is happening as the teacher makes a teapot from clay.	Make coil pots with clay. Explain the changes. Make a spiky clay hedgehog. Explain the changes.	Make thumb pots. Explain the changes. Make a clay model from free choice. Paint it. Explain the changes.	● Explain how the shape of clay changes when it is rolled, squashed, pulled and flattened. ● Explain how they changed the colour of an object by painting it. ● Talk about the differences between a ball of clay and a finished model; compare different models. ● Use their senses to explore a natural material.

Context: THE HARDWARE STORE

The hardware store, haberdashery or DIY store is a great context through which to teach the variety and uses of materials. The next three lessons involve learning about texture, fabrics and the identification and recognition of common materials that the children are likely to come across in everyday life. The children are given opportunities to learn through investigative play, with a number of activities being set within the role-play area.

LESSON 1

OBJECTIVE

● To develop the vocabulary, particularly of texture, associated with a range of objects made from a variety of materials.

RESOURCES

Main teaching activity: a 1m² panel of soft wood, screws, nails, a hammer, a screwdriver.
Group activities: 1–5. A selection of materials (see Preparation). **1.** Paper, pencils. **3.** Embossed wallpaper, wax crayons.

Vocabulary

heavy, light, soft, hard, bristles, handle, bristly, rough, smooth, big, small, cold, warm, sticky, tickly, sharp, pointed, curved, bendy

PREPARATION

Set up the 'hardware store' role-play area in a section of your classroom. Include items such as tools (not sharp), screws, nails, kitchen accessories, wallpaper, ceramic tiles, carpet and cushioned flooring tiles, curtains, cushions, shelving, shower curtain, taps, paintbrushes and a rubber mat. Start some nail and screw holes in a 1m² panel of soft wood.

INTRODUCTION

Talk to the children about the rules for playing in the hardware store. Explain the importance of taking great care when handling tools such as a hammer, a screwdriver, nails and screws. They should carry out these activities under supervision only. You may prefer to use plastic toy versions of the tools for the children to use unsupervised.

Show the children a nail and a screw. Ask them to tell you how these are alike and how they are different. Suggest that they are both sharp because they have points, but the nail is smooth while the screw has a thread. Ask the children whether they know what nails and screws are used for. Show them how to use the hammer and the screwdriver safely. Let one or two children hammer and screw some nails and screws into the wood, talking about how it feels.

MAIN TEACHING ACTIVITY

Pass a paintbrush around the circle of children and encourage them to feel the handle and bristles. Show them what you mean by 'bristles'. Tell them that the bristles are 'rough' and 'bristly'. Do any of them think the bristles are 'tickly' or 'itchy'? Tell them that the handle is 'smooth'. Invite a child to find something else in your collection that is smooth. Put this next to the paintbrush handle. Ask another child to find something that is 'rough' or 'tickly'. Place this item next to the bristles. Find other things from your collection that are partly smooth and partly rough, and put them together in a line (as in a matching dominoes game). An example is illustrated on the left.

GROUP ACTIVITIES

1. Ask an adult helper to sort the items with groups of four children. The children should choose items that are smooth or rough from the collection, sort them into two groups and record the groups by drawing.
2. Introduce other describing words to the children by using them to sort items in the collection – for example, soft and hard, cold and warm, heavy and light, stiff and bendy.
3. Ask the children to make wax crayon rubbings of embossed wallpaper.
4. Choose a texture-describing word (see Vocabulary) and make a daily display of items that have this texture.
5. Allow a group of children to play in the 'hardware store' role-play area.

DIFFERENTIATION

Play 'material dominoes' with the more able children. Choose an item whose texture can be described in two ways (for example, a brick is rough and hard)

and place it on a table. Invite each child in turn to find an item that can match one property (such as a nail, which is hard and smooth) to continue a line of textures, and to name the material from which the item is made.

Ask less able children to find items that match one describing word for each day.

ASSESSMENT

During Group activity 2, ask the children to choose an item from the 'hardware store', draw it and write a list of words to describe it (either independently or with an adult acting as scribe).

PLENARY

Ask the group who made the wax rubbings to talk about what they did. Pass the wallpaper around for the children to feel the texture. Ask them how they can tell that this is a good surface to make a rubbing of. Make a list of other materials and objects that would be good to make rubbings of, such as tree bark and a stone wall.

OUTCOMES

- Can use pictures to record what they have done.
- Can use simple language to describe texture.
- Can use their sense of touch to explore items found in the home.

LINKS

Across the curriculum: this lesson links (through sorting and making lists) with work on gathering information in ICT. The children are also developing their language and literacy skills by extending their vocabulary.

LESSON 2

Objective	● To use the senses to explore, sort and identify the materials from which various objects are made.
Resources	A collection of objects from around the classroom made from paper, wood, plastic and metal (include a paintbrush, hammer, cushion, screwdriver, tap and curtain); offcuts of woodchip wallpaper, ordinary paper, fabric, cardboard (including tubes), plastic and foil; gravel; scissors, adhesive; photocopiable page 115 (see Differentiation), pencils.
Main activity	Show the children the collection of objects. Choose one that is made from paper and ask the children to find others made from the same material. Together, arrange offcuts of paper and cardboard to make a pattern. Sort the items in your collection according to their colour, transparency or shininess. Can the children think of other ways in which the materials look the same or different? Set up Group play activities with adult supervision: **1.** Let the children make individual collage pictures using gravel and offcuts of paper, cardboard (including tubes), fabric, metal foil, woodchip and plastic. Encourage them to write, or scribe for them, words to describe how the materials in their pictures feel. **2.** Allow a group to play in the 'hardware store' role-play area. **3.** Let a group make a large picture or model of a metal-eating robot. Give them a selection of objects, some magnetic and some not. Give them a magnet and ask them to feed their robot, explaining that he only eats some metal items. (Do not include any aluminium cans in the collection, as they will not be attracted by the magnet.)
Differentiation	Ask the more able children to make a survey of your collection and identify the materials from which the objects are made. They can use photocopiable page 115 as a survey sheet, entering a tick for each material they can identify as part of each item. Make one copy and add any pictures of items in your collection not included on the sheet before photocopying enough for the group. Work with small groups of less able children, sorting the objects into sets of the same material. Look at one material at a time, and do not move on to another group until you are sure the children are able to complete the task.
Assessment	As you work with the different groups, note those children who do not contribute to the discussions and target them for smaller groups in the next lesson. Keep the survey sheets as evidence of children's ability to identify familiar materials.
Plenary	Make a 'feeling wall' from the children's pictures and describing words. Talk about the different materials in each 'brick', and the creative ways in which the children have arranged their materials.
Outcomes	● Know that there are many different materials. ● Know that different materials have different textures and look different. ● Can sort familiar materials by name.

LESSON 3

OBJECTIVE

● To recognise common materials and learn their names: wood, paper, fabric, metal.

RESOURCES

Main teaching activity: Wallpaper, sugar paper, a staple-gun, a display board, a table; a collection of cardboard boxes, paper-wrapped items, books and magazines.
Group activities: 1, 2 and 3. A collection of items made from wood, fabric and metal; a display board and table for each material; kitchen foil, curtain material, a staple-gun, scissors, adhesive, magazines with pictures of wooden and metal objects; labels, a felt-tipped pen. **4.** Coloured paper, scissors, adhesive, a display board. **5.** Four large sheets of paper; magazines with pictures of objects made from wood, metal, fabric or paper.

> *Vocabulary*
> metal, fabric, paper, cardboard, wood, wooden

PREPARATION

Collect items, and magazine pictures of items, made from wood, fabric, metal and paper.

INTRODUCTION

Tell the children that you are going to set up a display of different materials. Explain that you are going to put all the items made from the same material together.

MAIN TEACHING ACTIVITY

Select some wallpaper from the 'hardware store' and ask the children what material it is made from. If they do not know, tell them that it is made from paper. Staple the wallpaper to the display board and cover a table with sheets of sugar paper. Ask the children to look around the room for different kinds of paper. Talk about the thickness and texture of the papers before stapling them to the display board. Display a range of cardboard boxes, paper-wrapped objects, books and magazines on the table, and invite the children to add to this display at a later date.

GROUP ACTIVITIES

Repeat the Main teaching activity in small groups for wood, fabric and metal, allowing each group to choose a material.
1. Take some curtain material or other fabric item from the store, spread it over a display table and staple some to a board. Ask the children what this material is. Some may say that it is 'material'. Explain that the name of this material is 'fabric'. Ask the children to find other fabric items from the 'hardware store' and around the classroom (such as cushions, soft toys, rugs, bean bags and towels) and arrange them across the table, stapling some to the display board.
2. Use kitchen foil to cover the display board and table before arranging metal and wooden items on it. Ask the children to cut pictures of items made from wood and metal from magazines and add them to the display. They should write labels for each collection that describe the properties of all the items in it: 'shiny', 'smooth', 'I can see my face in it' and so on.
3. Ask an adult helper to play a 'Find the odd one out' game with groups of four children. The helper puts out two items made from the same material and one made from a different one, then asks the children to point to the odd material out.
4. Ask the children to make paper decorations to hang from a display board, make paper fans and wrap gifts. Talk with them about how the paper will fold, curl, bend and spread out.
5. Organise four large sheets of paper for the children to stick pictures of items made from wood, metal, fabric or paper. Ask an adult helper to work with this group to make sure each picture is stuck to the correct sheet.

DIFFERENTIATION

Make a display of each material with less able children, choosing a different material each week (first paper, then fabric and so on) and adding to the display every day. Include pictures of objects made from the chosen material. Repeat the Group activities with a different material per week – for example, cutting out pictures of one material and sticking them to one large sheet of paper that is added to each day.
Play the 'Odd material out' game with more able children, using five objects each time. Challenge them to devise a set of objects for their friends to find the odd material out.

ASSESSMENT

During the Group activities, ask the children in turn to find an object made from metal, wood, paper or fabric, and make a note of those who are successful. This will allow you to organise additional activities to reinforce the knowledge and understanding for those who are not always able to recognise a particular material.

PLENARY

Make a collection of items from each of the materials in the displays. Hold up each one in turn and ask the children which display it belongs to. Invite the children to bring non-precious things from home to add to the display.

OUTCOMES

- Can recognise paper, fabric, metal and wood.
- Can sort materials into named groups.
- Can begin to describe the properties of wood, metal, fabric and paper.

LINKS

Across the curriculum: this lesson requires the children to co-operate and work together to create the displays, and so contributes to their personal, social and emotional development.

Context: THE WATER TRAY

The water tray is used well in most Reception classes. The next three lessons are examples of how planned, focused practical activities can provide a good context through which to develop scientific skills, knowledge and understanding.

LESSON 4

OBJECTIVE

- To learn that soap and water mixed together make bubbles.

RESOURCES

Main teaching activity: Bubble mixture, bubble blowers, 'no tears' bubble bath, a water tray.
Group activities: 1. A bowl or bucket, water, 'no tears' bubble bath and shampoo. **2.** Hand-held whisks. **3.** Circle templates, paper, pencils, paints. **4.** Soap flakes, water. **5.** Paint pots, straws, 'no tears' bubble bath, water, blank paper. Provide other bubble sources (such as washing-up liquid) for more able children to experiment with.

Vocabulary

bubbles, mix, water, soap, liquid, round, float, mixture

PREPARATION

Practise mixing bubble bath mixture, making sure that it is the correct consistency to blow bubbles. You may wish to let the children play with the bubble mixture for several days before doing these activities, as there is usually a great deal of excitement.

INTRODUCTION

Sit the children in a circle so that they can all see the bubbles. Blow a few bubbles from a bottle of bubble mixture and let the children catch them as they float to the ground.

MAIN TEACHING ACTIVITY

While the children are watching, use 'no tears' bubble bath and water to make a bubble mixture. Explain that when a 'soapy' material is mixed with water, bubbles can be made. Invite one or two children to blow bubbles with the new mixture. Show the children the 'no tears' shampoo and washing-up liquid. Tell them that they are going to work in groups, mixing each of the 'soapy' things with water to make bubbles.

GROUP ACTIVITIES

1. Work with pairs or groups of three. Place a bowl or bucket, half-filled with warm water, in the centre of a table. Add the bubble bath or shampoo to the container, and let the children take turns to make bubbles by agitating the water. Challenge the groups to see who can make the bubbles 'grow' over the top of the bowl or bucket, using fresh water each time and alternating the two 'soapy' materials.

2. Allow a group of children to make bubble sculptures with the mixture in the water tray, using their hands or hand-held whisks to agitate the mixture.

3. Ask the children to use circle templates to draw pictures of bubbles. Display these on a board with the title 'Soap and water make bubbles'.

4. Ask an adult helper to show the children how to mix soap flakes and water while washing their hands, and how to blow bubbles from the frothy mix.

5. Let the children make bubble patterns, using a mixture of paint and 'no tears' bubble bath in a paint pot. They should blow through a straw until the bubbles rise above the pot, then quickly make a print of the bubble pattern by placing a piece of paper on top of the pot before the bubbles all go 'pop'.

DIFFERENTIATION

Allow less able children time to play with the mixtures, then ask questions such as: *What is happening? What can you see? What are you doing to make the bubbles grow?* to develop their understanding and thinking skills. Tell them that the soap mixed with the water is making the bubbles.

More able children could investigate different soap mixtures: *If you add more bubble bath to the mixture, do you get bigger bubbles? Do you get the same results if you mix washing-up liquid with water? Is the cheaper brand as good as the more expensive brand?* Take care that the children do not get the mixture in their eyes.

ASSESSMENT

Encourage the children to talk about what they are doing, and listen to their conversations. This is an activity where incidental chat will tell you a great deal about the children's understanding. A few simple questions will direct their thinking.

PLENARY

Ask the group who made the bubble patterns with paint to talk about what they did. Cut around a few prints that are dry and add them to your display. Ask: *Can you see where a bubble popped on the paper? How can you tell?*

OUTCOMES

● Know that soap mixes with water.
● Know that mixing soap and water together makes bubbles.
● Are able to co-operate, work together, share and take turns.

LINKS

Across the curriculum: this lesson is good for developing social skills, as the children are encouraged to work together and take turns through a series of activities. They are also given lots of opportunities to talk about what they are doing and to ask questions. Discussion of soap and detergents can also be linked to hygiene and health.

LESSON 5

Objectives	● To investigate what happens when we try to mix oil and water. ● To learn that not all liquids mix with water.
Resources	Cooking oil, water-based food colouring, an A4-sized water tray, a sheet of absorbent A4 paper (such as blotting paper); jars of cold water and different kinds of oil (such as motor oil, olive oil and coloured bath oils).
Main activity	Try out the demonstration first to gauge how much food colouring and oil you need to use. 　Tell the children that you are going to find out what happens when you try to mix oil and water. Pour some water into the tray. Show them the cooking oil and explain that you are going to pour the oil onto the water. Do this, then ask the children what they can see. *Is the oil floating or sinking? Is it staying on top of the water or going to the bottom, or is it mixing with the water?* Mix some food colouring into the mixture so that the children can see the result more clearly (only the water will take up the colour). Invite a child to give the mixture a good stir, making sure that he or she does not get oil on his or her clothes. Carefully place a sheet of absorbent A4 paper onto the top of the tray to soak up the oil. *What has happened? Where has the oil gone? Has it disappeared?* Look at the pattern on the paper. 　Repeat the activity with groups of four children. Let each child make his or her own oil pattern. 　Half-fill some jars with cold water. Look at different oils and talk about their colours and relative thickness. Add drops of different kinds of oil to each jar, then replace the lids. Carefully give each jar a shake and watch what happens to the oil. Look for colours spreading in the water.
Differentiation	Half-fill some jars with warm water and add drops of oil. Talk with more able children about whether the oil reacts differently with warm water. *Does it still float to the top?* Talk with less able children to help them explain what the oil does. For example: *Does it mix with the water, sink to the bottom, float in the middle or float on top?* Point to the top, middle and bottom of the jar as you ask these questions to show the children what you mean by 'sink' and 'float'.
Assessment	Observe the children as they watch the oil in the jar and record those who understand that the oil and water do not mix.
Plenary	Talk about the need to be careful when using oil. *What would happen if the oil got onto our clothes? If oil and water do not mix, how can we get oil out of our clothes?* Some children may be able to talk about oil slicks and the effects these have on birds. *How can we remove the oil from a bird's feathers?* Explain that soap and detergent mix with oil and with water, and so make it possible to wash away oil.
Outcomes	● Know that oil and water do not mix. ● Know that oils can have different colours, and some oils are thicker than others. ● Know that oil floats on water.

LESSON 6

OBJECTIVES
● To learn that the thicker a mixture is, the harder it is to stir.
● To learn that the more water is added, the runnier a mixture becomes.

RESOURCES
Main teaching activity: Cornflour, water, a mixing bowl, a wooden spoon, a tray.
Group activities: 1. Four bowls with different mixtures (see Preparation), a hand-held whisk, a rotary whisk, a metal spoon, a wooden spoon, a stick. **2.** Paper, cornflour mixture. **3.** Different liquid foods (such as syrup and jam), metal spoons. **4.** Paints, paper; squeezy bottles or straws.

PREPARATION
Mix cornflour, food colouring and water to make four bowls with different consistencies of mixture. Only use one of each colour, so that the children will have a colour to refer to when discussing the mixtures. Do not make any mixture too thick, or it will harden and not stir.

INTRODUCTION
Settle the children around a table on which you have a bowl, water, cornflour and a wooden spoon. Pour about half a litre of water into the bowl and slowly mix in the cornflour to a smooth consistency, adding one spoonful at a time. Add food colouring if you wish. As you mix the cornflour and water, talk about the thickness of the mixture, whether it runs off the spoon and how it becomes thicker and less runny as you add more cornflour.

Vocabulary
thick, thicker, thickest, thin, thinner, thinnest, runny, runnier, runniest, consistency, hard to stir, easy to stir, harder, hardest, easier, easiest

MAIN TEACHING ACTIVITY

Pass the bowl around and allow the children to stir the mixture. Discuss what it feels like when stirring the mixture. *Is it stiff or runny? Is it hard or easy to stir?* Collect a spoonful of the mixture and let it dribble onto a tray, making a pattern. Talk about the movement of the mixture. *Does it drip in blobs, or does it stick together in a line? How could we make the mixture thicker? How could we make it runnier?*

GROUP ACTIVITIES

1. Work with four children at a time, stirring the mixtures and talking about their texture and consistency. Work out together which colour mixture is the easiest and the most difficult to stir, then put the mixtures in order. As the children stir the thinnest mixture, ask them questions such as: *Is this mixture the easiest to stir? How easy is it to stir?* Repeat the questions with the other mixtures.

2. Ask an adult helper to do cornflour finger painting with the children, encouraging them to feel the mixture running through their fingers and to talk about its consistency.

3. Set up a table of different liquid foods (such as syrup, jam and water) for the children to explore by stirring or blending with various objects and machines, then letting the mixture run back into the container.

4. Ask the children to make pictures by dripping paint on paper and making curled streaks of paint. They can either use 'squeezy bottles' (such as empty washing-up liquid bottles) or dip a straw into the paint and then let the paint fall out.

DIFFERENTIATION

Ask the more able group to say which of the mixtures has the most cornflour just by their thickness. Let them make their own mixtures of water and cornflour; challenge them to make a runnier or thicker mixture than the ones you have made.

Work with pairs of less able children, so that they have an opportunity to explore and talk about the mixtures on a one-to-one basis. Provide some paint and let them use their fingers to spread the paint across a table (with a wipe-clean surface) to make pictures.

ASSESSMENT

Assess the children's use of language, and particularly their comparisons. Do they understand the difference between 'thick' and 'thin' mixtures? Note those children who understand that to make a mixture thinner, you need to add more liquid.

PLENARY

Make a collection of liquids to reinforce the children's understanding of what a liquid is.

OUTCOMES

● Know that a mixture can be thin (runny) or thick (stiff).
● Can compare the thickness of two mixtures, and order mixtures by how thin or thick they are.
● Recognise some of the physical properties of liquids.

LINKS

Between units: this lesson links with the Assessment activity in Unit 7, Lesson 9, involving making different colours of icing for biscuits.

Context: THE SAND TRAY

The sand tray, like the water tray, lends itself well to work in the early years. The next lesson shows how this resource can be used for focused, planned development of early skills in scientific investigation.

LESSON 7

Objective	● To learn that sand, when mixed with the right amount of water, will stick together. ● To learn that dry sand does not stick together. ● To learn that damp or wet sand is made by mixing dry sand with water.
Resources	Buckets, spades, moulds (including one that is transparent), dry sand in a sand tray, damp sand in a shallow tray. Make sure the sand has the right consistency for making good sandcastles.
Main activity	Put some dry sand in a shallow tray and pass it around for the children to feel its texture. Encourage them to use phrases such as 'dry', 'runs through the fingers', 'gritty' and 'rough'. Mix some water with the sand to make it damp. Pass the tray around again and ask the children how the texture has changed. Encourage them to use words such as 'damp', 'wet', 'cold' and 'sticks together'. *How has it stayed the same?* (It is still gritty and rough.) Ask them to grab a handful of the sand and to squeeze it tightly so that the sand sticks together. Talk about what has happened. 　Fill the transparent container with damp sand, talking to the children all the time about how the sand is filling the container so that there is no space left inside. When the container is full, press the sand in tightly so that it is well stuck together. Turn the container over, and ask the children what they think will happen when you remove the container. They may suggest that there will be a sandcastle left in the same shape as the container. Demonstrate this. 　Organise Group activities with adult support: **1.** Ask an adult helper to work with four children at a time, mixing dry sand and water to make the right consistency to make perfect sandcastles. **2.** Look at some sand mixed with too much water. Challenge the children to build a sandcastle with this mixture. Can they explain why they did not succeed? **3.** Allow the children to play with a range of buckets and moulds (including a transparent mould) to make sandcastles. Ask them to predict the shape of each sandcastle before they remove the bucket or mould. Can they match each finished castle to the correct container?
Differentiation	Some children may not have the strength and physical dexterity to do this activity unaided, and may need the support of an adult. Give more able children some dry sand and talk to them about the differences and similarities between the two textures. Do they understand that they cannot make sandcastles with dry sand because it does not stick together, but flows like a liquid? Can they mix the right amount of water with the sand to make a good material for building sandcastles?
Assessment	Note those children who understand that the damp sand sticks together, and so remains in the shape of the container that it has filled.
Plenary	Talk about which children managed to make a sandcastle. *Who made the biggest sandcastle?* Ask the child in question to fetch the container from which it was made. *Did anyone build one sandcastle on top of another?* Demonstrate this to the children by making a tower of sandcastles.
Outcomes	● Know that damp sand sticks together. ● Know that you mix dry sand and water to make damp sand. ● Know the similarities and differences between dry and damp sand. ● Can describe what damp sand feels like.

Context: THE BAKER'S SHOP

The next four lessons are set in the context of a baker's shop and focus on making bread, biscuits, cakes and pies. Although I have used specific items for these lessons, the food items made can be changed to fit each school's circumstances. For example, the children could make sweets of other cultures instead of cakes or biscuits.

LESSON 8

OBJECTIVE
● To learn that the shape of a mixture can be changed by rolling.

RESOURCES

Main teaching activity: A copy of the traditional story 'The Gingerbread Man'; a mixing bowl, a wooden spoon, a rolling pin, a pastry board, pastry cutters, an oven, baking trays; flour, margarine, milk. You will need various biscuit and cake ingredients for the follow-up lessons; the recipes on photocopiable page 116 may be useful.
Group activities: 1, 2 and 4. Cooking utensils and ingredients as for Main teaching activity.
3. Play dough, rolling pins.

Vocabulary
rolling, flat, flatter, spread out, shape, change, mixture

PREPARATION

Make up a fresh lot of play dough.

INTRODUCTION

Read the story of 'The Gingerbread Man' to the children. Talk about the ingredients that were used to make the biscuit man. Do the children think the gingerbread biscuit was tasty? Why do they think this?

MAIN TEACHING ACTIVITY

Working with groups of children, mix the ingredients to make dough at the right consistency to roll out. Show the children the ball of dough and talk about its shape and size. Ask them how you could make the ball of dough flat so that you could make flat biscuits. Flatten the dough with your hands, explaining that you are squashing the mixture flat. Use a rolling pin to roll out the mixture to the correct thickness (let the children say when this is), explaining that you are now pushing the mixture out to make a different, flatter shape. Ask the children to describe the size and shape of the mixture now. Make sure they understand that there is the same amount of mixture as before.

Repeat the activity over the next week. On day 1 you could make gingerbread biscuits, on day 2 jam tarts, on day 3 chocolate biscuits, on day 4 mince pies and on day 5 a peach flan. Talk each day about whether the mixture is easy or difficult to stir, whether it sticks together when milk or water is added, and whether it changes its shape when squashed or rolled out.

GROUP ACTIVITIES

1. Ask an adult helper to work with groups of four children, making a biscuit or pastry mix. Prompt the adult to talk about how the mixture is ready to be rolled out when it sticks together.
2. When the mixture is ready, you should repeat the Main teaching activity with small groups of children.

3. Let groups of six children play with play dough, making biscuits, jam tarts and other play food. Let them flatten the mixture with their hands as well as using rolling pins.
4. Allow four children to play in the 'baker's shop' role-play area.

DIFFERENTIATION

In the follow-up lessons, allow more able children to follow simple recipe cards (perhaps copied from page 116, with additional pictures provided) to make their biscuits and cakes with little supervision. Question them to find out why they are rolling out their mixture.

ASSESSMENT

Ask the children to draw four pictures to show the ingredients being mixed, the mixture sticking together, the mixture being rolled out to change its shape and the finished biscuit or cake. Keep these pictures as evidence of the children's understanding.

PLENARY
Let the children enjoy the biscuits with milk at snack time. Make a large chart to show the four steps outlined in the Assessment section.

OUTCOMES
- Know that squashing and rolling-out change the shape of dough.
- Know that dry ingredients will mix together.
- Know that dry ingredients will stick together when mixed with a liquid.

LINKS

Across the curriculum: this lesson develops physical dexterity skills through stirring with a spoon and using a rolling pin to roll out the mixture. The children should use their senses of smell and taste to evaluate the quality of the finished biscuits and cakes.

LESSON 9

Objective	To learn that the shape of materials can be changed by squashing, pulling and bending.
Resources	A recipe for pizza dough (see photocopiable page 117), flour, water, yeast, olive oil; an oven or microwave oven, a jar of pizza topping, a tin of tomatoes, cheese, a cheese grater, cooked sausages, pineapple rings, a knife, a chopping board, a ready-made pizza, play dough.
Main activity	Check for allergies. Make enough dough (with the children's help if you wish to reinforce previous learning objectives) for each child to have a piece the size of a tennis ball. Show the children a ready-made pizza and ask them what ingredients they can see. Make a list of all the things they say, then add any things that they have omitted. Explain that before you can put the topping on a pizza, you must first make the base. Place a ball of dough on a board and talk about its size and shape. What does the finished shape need to look like? The children may say that you need to flatten the dough into a shape like a plate. Demonstrate how you could make the base of the pizza in this way. Now say that you have another way of making it. Slowly roll the dough into a long sausage shape, pulling it out from time to time. Ask the children how long they think the sausage needs to be. When the dough is about as thick as your thumb, stop rolling and look at the size and shape again. Pull the dough out into a straight line. Coil the sausage shape into a disc (see illustration) and press the edges together to make a pizza base. Place the base on a plate and cook in an oven for ten minutes. Organise Group activities with adult support: **1.** Make the pizza bases with groups of six children, reinforcing what they are doing to change the shape of the dough. **2.** Ask an adult helper to supervise the children closely as they grate cheese for the topping. Make sure the adult does not let the children grate small pieces of cheese, in case their fingers get too close to the grater. If necessary, the adult should grate and the children should watch. The adult should talk with the children about what is happening to the cheese. **3.** Ask a group to mix together tinned tomatoes and a jar of pizza topping. Use this to reinforce their learning about mixing substances together. **4.** Ask a group to cut the pineapple rings and sausages into pieces. Talk about the changing shapes of these food items. **5.** The children could practise making coils with play dough.
Differentiation	Give those children who are having difficulty one-to-one support. Some may not have the dexterity to form the dough into a long sausage shape.
Assessment	Note those children who can work independently and know how to roll and flatten the dough. Listen to the children's chat as they work to hear the vocabulary they are using. Question the children to find out their level of understanding.
Plenary	Together, put the toppings on the pizzas. With the children well back, cook the pizzas (in batches) until they are golden brown, then remove them and let them cool. Let the children enjoy the finished pizzas.
Outcomes	Know that the shape of dough can be changed by squashing, rolling and coiling round.

LESSON 10

Objective	• To learn that some dry ingredients will mix with water and that when you add more water, the mixture becomes runnier.
Resources	Ingredients for making batches of small cakes, a microwave oven, icing sugar, an icing bag, food colouring, chocolate, biscuits; dried pulses, flour, sugar, powder paint, salt, pots of water.

Main activity	Make batches of cakes with groups of children, reinforcing learning objectives from the previous lessons in this unit. Add food colouring and chocolate to the mixtures, so that each group makes cakes of a different colour. Watch the changes that take place.
	   Ask groups of six to eight children to ice the cakes. Mix the icing together, and change the colour by adding food colouring or chocolate to each mixture. Allow the children to spread the icing onto the cakes with a knife. When it is dry, use an icing bag to squeeze blobs of different-coloured icing onto the centre of each cake. Ask the children which colour food colouring was added to the icing.
	   Let the children work with an adult helper to make faces on biscuits with icing sugar.
	   Put a range of dry materials (pulses, flour, sugar, powder paint, salt) out with pots of water, and let the children investigate whether each dry material will mix with water.

Differentiation	Talk about the word 'dissolve' with more able children when talking about the activities. Ask them to sort the dry materials into sets according to whether they dissolve (that is, become invisible) in water. (Sugar and salt will dissolve, the others will not.) Less able children should have the experience of icing their cakes in order to feel how the icing squeezes out of the bag, sticks to the cake and spreads across its surface. They may then be ready to talk about the consistency of the icing during the biscuit-decorating activity.
Assessment	Listen to the children as they ice the cakes. How many ask questions and comment on how the mixture feels? Do they use words such as 'spread', 'mixture', 'runny' and 'thin' to describe the mixture? Ask: *What makes the mixture spread easily?* Does anyone see a relationship between the thickness of the mixture and the ease with which it spreads?
Plenary	Talk about the dry materials that do and do not mix with water. Sort them into two sets. Ask the children to find other things (under adult supervision) at home or in school that will mix with water.
Outcomes	• Know that icing sugar will mix with water. • Know that when water mixes with a dry ingredient, the mixture is wet. • Know that a cake mixture changes when cooked. • Know that the colour of icing changes when food colouring is added.

LESSON 11

OBJECTIVE
• To learn that the texture of a mixture can be changed by cooking.

RESOURCES
Main teaching activity: A copy of 'Goldilocks and The Three Bears', instant porridge oats, milk, a bowl, a cup, a spoon, a microwave oven.
Group activities: 1. Sugar, salt, porridge oats, milk, a microwave oven, three bowls, several spoons. **2.** A recipe and ingredients for oat biscuits (photocopiable page 118). **3.** Photocopiable page 119, scissors, adhesive sticks, paper, pencils. **4.** Paper, pencils, paints. **5.** A table with bowls and spoons in three sizes. **7.** Various ingredients and cooking utensils.

> *Vocabulary*
> dry, wet, heat, cook, liquid, microwave oven

PREPARATION
Move the microwave oven to the classroom and carry out a risk assessment.

INTRODUCTION
Read the story of 'The Three Bears'. Say that porridge should never be touched when it is cooking on the stove, and should be left to cool down otherwise. Emphasise that the mouth is easily burned.

MAIN TEACHING ACTIVITY
Pass the oats around in a bowl and invite the children to feel the texture. Next, pass milk around in a cup for the children to dip a finger into. Tell the children that you are going to mix a dry

ingredient, the oats, with a liquid ingredient, the milk, to make porridge. Mix the oats and milk and show the children the runny mixture. Ask them whether the oats have mixed with the milk as the icing sugar did with the water. *How do the two mixtures look different?*

Put the porridge mixture in the microwave oven and cook it, giving it an occasional stir, until it has a smooth consistency. Show the mixture to the children, stirring it to show the new texture. When the mixture is cool, allow the children to stir it so that they can feel the difference in the texture. Ask them to explain what has happened to the mixture. *What has made it change?* Talk about how the heat from the microwave oven has changed the texture of the mixture: it has helped the dry oats and the liquid milk to mix together.

GROUP ACTIVITIES

1. Make porridge with groups of six children. When the porridge is cool enough, empty it into three bowls and add salt to one, sugar to another and nothing to the third. Invite the children to taste each one and say which is their favourite.
2. Ask an adult helper to make oat biscuits using the recipe on photocopiable page 118 with groups of six children for the class to enjoy at snack time.
3. Give the children a copy each of page 119. Ask them to cut out the four pictures and stick them down on another sheet of paper in the correct order (in two rows).
4. Ask the children to paint or draw pictures of the three bears eating their porridge.
5. Organise a table with three different-sized bowls and spoons piled up. Ask the children to lay the table for the three bears' breakfast.
6. Make a list of other foods that change when cooked, such as apples, potatoes, cakes or bread.
7. Make other snacks with the children to reinforce the learning objective, such as rice pudding, custard or pancakes.

DIFFERENTIATION

Ask the more able children to make a pictogram showing the children's favourite porridge topping from Group activity 1.

ASSESSMENT

Use Group activity 3 to assess the children's understanding of the process of cooking porridge.

PLENARY

Talk about which porridge topping the children liked best and record their choices on a tick chart. Decide which is the class' favourite porridge topping.

OUTCOMES

● Know that the way porridge looks changes when it is cooked.
● Know that porridge has a different texture when cooked.
● Know that heat is used to cook things.
● Know that we should never touch hot things, as they can burn us.

LINKS

Across the curriculum: this lesson links to personal, social and emotional development through personal hygiene and washing of hands, taking care not to touch the hot porridge, and making a choice of a favourite porridge topping.

ASSESSMENT

LESSON 12

OBJECTIVE

● To find out what the children know about changing the shape of materials.

RESOURCES

Main assessment activity: A collection of ceramic ornaments and pots, a cup, a teapot, balls of clay, a board or piece of non-stick flooring, pots of water. **Assessment activities 2–5.** As above; a rolling pin, a work area with easily washable flooring (these are messy activities – an outside area is best).

PREPARATION

Make a collection of ceramic items. Make enough balls of clay (about the size of a tennis ball) for each child to have one, and place them in an airtight container to keep them moist. If necessary, wrap each ball separately in cling film.

INTRODUCTION

Show the children some of the ceramic items in your collection. Ask them to think of words to describe these items. Ask questions such as: *How would you make the spout for the teapot? How do you think the handle was put on the cup?* Ask the children whether they think the teapot started out looking like this, or looked different in any way. When they have finished expressing their opinions, show them a ball of clay.

MAIN ASSESSMENT ACTIVITY

Ask the children whether they believe you when you say that the teapot probably started out looking like this ball of clay. Some will, but many will not. Remove three small pieces of clay from the ball. Show the children how to make a bowl shape by pushing into the clay with your thumbs. Talk about how the shape of the bowl is changing. Next, roll out a piece of clay and attach it for the handle. Roll out another piece for the spout, and finally flatten a piece of clay for the lid. Ask the children what you are doing, and what is happening to the shape of the clay, at each stage. This will provide you with information about the children's understanding of how the shape of the clay is being changed. Use words such as 'pull', 'roll', 'push' and 'flatten'. Ask the children how you could make the teapot look a different colour, and note their suggestions.

ASSESSMENT ACTIVITY 2

Make coil pots with the children. Ask them to explain what is happening to the clay as they roll it out to make a long sausage shape. As they coil the length into a pot shape, talk about how the shape of the clay is changing. At the end of the activity, ask the children to draw three pictures to show the different shapes of their clay.

ASSESSMENT ACTIVITY 3

Give the children a piece of clay and ask them to pull out bits to make the nose and spikes of a hedgehog. Ask them to describe what is happening to the clay as they pull out the spikes. Ask them to draw 'before' and 'after' pictures.

ASSESSMENT ACTIVITY 4

Show the children how to make thumb pots out of lumps of clay. Ask them to explain how the shape of the clay changes as they push into it with their thumbs.

ASSESSMENT ACTIVITY 5

Give the children a small ball of clay and ask them to make anything they like. When they have finished, ask them how they changed the shape of the clay to look like their finished article (name what each child has made). Let the children paint their finished models. Ask them to explain how they changed the colour of the items by painting. Encourage them to compare all the different models they have made.

Assessment outcomes

On completion of these Assessment activities, you should know which children have attained the following objectives to support the development of their knowledge and understanding of the world:
● Explain how the shape of clay changes when it is rolled, squashed, pulled and flattened.
● Explain how they changed the colour of an object by painting it.
● Talk about the differences between a ball of clay and a finished model in terms of shape, size and colour.
● Notice similarities and differences between different models.
● Use their senses to explore a natural material.

Name

What is it made of?

✓ the material.

	wood	metal	plastic	fabric

Recipes

Pastry recipe

230g plain flour
115g margarine
a pinch of salt
approximately 2 tablespoons cold water to mix

- Sieve the flour and salt into a mixing bowl.
- Rub the margarine into the flour with your fingertips.
- Add the water a little at a time and rub in.
- Gather the mixture into a ball.
- Roll out to the required thickness.

Ginger biscuit recipe

345g plain flour
2 level teaspoons ground ginger
115g butter
1 cup soft brown sugar
4 tablespoons golden syrup
1 egg

- Sift together the flour and ground ginger.
- Rub the butter into the mixture.
- Add the sugar and mix well.
- Beat the egg and warm the syrup slightly, then add them both to the mixture.
- Stir the ingredients together to make a pliable dough.
- Roll out and use a cutter to make the shape of gingerbread people.

UNIT 4 MATERIALS

Pizza base recipes

Pizza base (baking powder method)

   3 cups self-raising flour
   1 teaspoon baking powder
90g butter or margarine
   milk and water to mix

- Sift the flour and baking powder together.
- Rub in the butter or margarine and mix to a firm dough with milk and water.
- Turn onto a floured board and knead.

Pizza base (yeast and oil method)

   3 cups plain flour
   a pinch of salt
   1 tablespoon olive oil
   1 teaspoon dried yeast
   $\frac{1}{4}$ pint warm water

- Sieve the salt and flour into a basin.
- Make a hole in the centre and add the oil.
- Sprinkle the yeast into the water.
- Pour the yeast mixture over the oil.
- Sprinkle flour over the yeast mixture.
- Cover with a cloth and leave in a warm place for 15–20 minutes, until the yeast mixture starts to bubble.
- Blend all the ingredients together and knead until smooth.

Recipe for oat biscuits

230g oats
115g plain flour
115g sugar
115g margarine
    milk for mixing
    $\frac{1}{2}$ teaspoon baking powder
    a pinch of salt

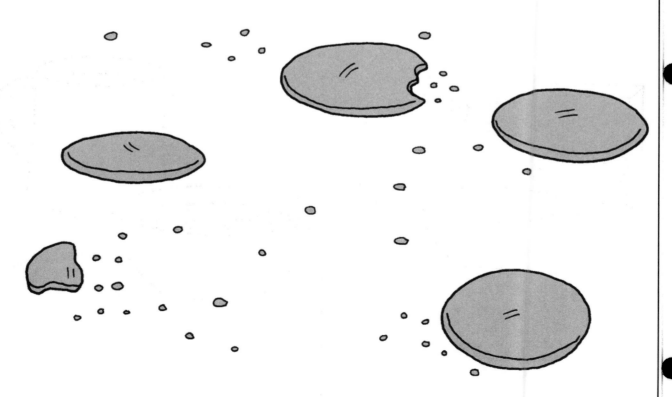

- Mix together the flour, oats, sugar, salt and baking powder.

- Rub in the margarine.

- Mix to a dry paste with the milk.

- Roll out to the required thickness.

- Cut into shapes.

- Bake for 30 minutes on medium heat.

UNIT 4 MATERIALS

Name

Making porridge

Making things work

ORGANISATION (7 LESSONS)

	OBJECTIVES	MAIN ACTIVITY	GROUP ACTIVITIES	PLENARY	OUTCOMES
LESSON 1	● To learn that electricity is dangerous.	Identify electrical switches, plugs and sockets. Talk about the dangers of electricity.	Attach 'Do not touch' stickers to plugs and sockets. Make posters about the dangers of electricity. Role-play a hairdresser's shop and a home.	Create a set of class rules about what the children may touch and what they must not.	● Know that electricity is not safe: it is dangerous. ● Know which electrical appliances they may touch and which they must never touch.
LESSON 2	● To learn that many electrical appliances have switches that need to be used safely. ● To begin to ask questions about how things work.	Practise turning on a range of electrical items that your school policy allows. Reinforce the dangers of electricity.		Attach 'Yes' and 'No' stickers to appliances to show whether the children are allowed to touch them.	● Know that switches allow electricity through to make things work. ● Know which switches are safe to touch and which should never be touched. ● Can ask questions about how things work.
LESSON 3	● To learn that a range of household appliances use electricity.	Sort a range of household electrical appliances by the room they are used in.	Repeat the sorting activity. Make models of electrical items for a model house. Play with a doll's house and in the home role-play area. Paint pictures of household items.	Make a large wall display with the children's pictures. Ask the children to talk about their work.	● Know that certain household appliances work by electricity. ● Can sort appliances according to the room they are usually found in. ● Can identify some household appliances that do not work by electricity.
LESSON 4	● To learn that electrical items may produce heat, sound, light and/or movement.	Sort electrical appliances by whether they produce sound, heat, light or movement. Label 'play' appliances.		Talk about how the appliances that have motors work.	● Know that electrical items can give out heat, light, sound and/or movement. ● Can sort objects according to given criteria. ● Can make drawings to record what they have found out.
LESSON 5	● To learn that a battery is a portable supply of electricity. ● To learn that some toys and other items are powered by batteries.	Talk about how the flash on a camera works. Talk about a range of items that use batteries.	Explore a range of items that work by battery. Identify things that work by battery and by mains electricity. Paint pictures of a favourite battery-operated toy. Find objects which work by battery. Play with battery-operated toys.	Talk about the paintings of battery-operated toys. Make a display of things that work by battery and things that do not.	● Can recognise batteries. ● Know that batteries are a source of power and that they make things work. ● Know that some things work by battery and others do not. ● Know that batteries can be dangerous if not handled properly.
LESSON 6	● To learn that many battery-operated items have a switch to turn them on and off.	Identify the switches on a variety of battery-operated items. Explore how these items are switched on and off.		Talk about a favourite battery-operated item. Invite the children to say how the switch makes it work.	● Can identify the switch on a battery-operated item. ● Know that a switch may be needed to make something work. ● Can record findings by making drawings. ● Can begin to describe the movement of familiar objects.

	OBJECTIVES	MAIN ACTIVITY	ACTIVITY 2	ACTIVITY 3	OUTCOMES
ASSESSMENT 7	● To assess the children's ability to identify and sort items by whether mains electricity or batteries power them. ● To assess the children's understanding of the dangers of electricity.	Sort items according to whether they work by mains electricity or batteries. Talk about how electricity is dangerous.	Identify items powered by mains electricity or by battery.	Sort items according to whether they work by electricity, batteries or neither.	● Know that some things work by mains electricity, some work by battery and some use neither. ● Identify whether a range of familiar objects work by battery or mains electricity. ● Know that electricity can be dangerous.

Context: MY HOME

The lessons in this unit can be taught through a topic on 'My home'. Set up the role-play area as a 'home', containing a kitchen, lounge and bedroom area (if possible). Allow the children to rearrange the furniture from time to time.

LESSON 1

OBJECTIVE
● To learn that electricity is dangerous.

RESOURCES

Main teaching activity: Electrical items including a table lamp, hairdryer and CD player or cassette recorder; stickers cut from photocopiable page 129, adhesive.
Group activities: 1. Photocopiable page 129, scissors, adhesive. **2.** Large sheets of paper, felt-tipped pens. **3.** Dolls, combs, hairbrushes, shampoo, conditioner, hand towels, a washbasin, a hairdryer. **4.** The 'home' role-play area, a range of toy household electrical items.

> *Vocabulary*
> dangerous, danger, electricity, electrical, switch, lead, socket, plug

PREPARATION

Colour and cut out two 'Do not touch' stickers from photocopiable page 129.

INTRODUCTION

Gather the children together so that they can see the lamp and a wall socket nearby. Ask them how you can make the light come on. Point out the plug, switch and lead on the lamp, then point out the wall socket as you plug in the lamp and switch it on. Tell the children that this something they must **not** do. Explain that the lamp works by electricity, which travels from the socket through the plug and lead to the bulb, making it light up. Explain that although electricity makes the lamp work, it is very dangerous and must never be touched. Explain the dangers of electric shocks and the class rules about electricity.

MAIN TEACHING ACTIVITY

Repeat the demonstration with the other electrical items. Point out the switch on the wall socket and the switch on the appliance that makes it work. Ask the children which part of the appliance they should never touch; after their response, attach 'Do not touch' stickers to the plug and the wall socket. Explain again that they should never touch these things because, once something is plugged in and switched on, electricity travels from the socket to make things work and this electricity is dangerous. It may be appropriate to tell the children that it is the electricity, not the appliance itself, that is dangerous: people have made the appliance safe by wrapping the wires in plastic and putting something called a fuse inside the plug. The concept of electricity is a difficult one, however, and children can easily become confused if explanations are too long.

GROUP ACTIVITIES

1. Ask an adult helper to work with six children to cut out stickers from copies of photocopiable page 129 and attach them to electrical plugs and wall sockets in the classroom.
2. Work with groups of six children to make large posters about the dangers of electricity. Display these prominently in the classroom.
3. Set up a 'hairdresser's shop' role-play area for the children to comb, shampoo and dry the dolls' hair.
4. Allow four children to play in the 'home' role-play area. Put out as many toy household electrical items as you can for them to use: cooker, iron, TV, heater, telephone, shower, lamp and so on. Emphasise that the children must not touch the real items.

DIFFERENTIATION

Talk to more able children about the path that the electricity takes. Point out the socket and its switch, then the plug, lead and switch on the appliance. Explain that when the switches are 'on', it allows electricity to flow from the socket through the plug and lead to make the appliance work.

Less able children should repeat the activity over a number of days until they fully understand that they should never touch plugs, switches or sockets.

ASSESSMENT

Watch the children as they ask an adult to attach their stickers to things around the classroom. Note those who show awareness of the dangers of electricity by putting their stickers in appropriate places.

PLENARY

At the end of the activities, work with the whole class to write a set of class rules about what the children are and are not allowed to touch (with particular reference to plugs and switches).

OUTCOMES

- Know that electricity is not safe: it is dangerous.
- Know which electrical appliances they may touch and which they must not touch.

LINKS

Between units: this lesson links to Unit 1, Lesson 6 on hazardous substances and to Unit 8, Lesson 6 on awareness of the dangers of sunlight.
Across the curriculum: a link with personal, social and emotional development is made through the children's growing awareness of how to keep themselves and others safe.

LESSON 2

Objectives	● To learn that many electrical appliances have switches that need to be used safely. ● To begin to ask questions about how things work.
Resources	A computer, cassette recorder and any other items (including light switches) in your classroom that you want the children to use independently; sticky labels, a felt-tipped pen. Make sure that the items in your collection actually work!
Main activity	With groups of four to six children, sit around the computer. Talk about the dangers of electricity, and reinforce the learning from the previous lesson. Explain to the children that they are going to learn how to turn the computer and monitor on by using the correct switches. If you want them to do this only under adult supervision at all times, explain this. Ask an adult helper to show other groups how to operate a cassette recorder and other appliances in the classroom. Talk about safety and explain that switches are for turning a machine on and off; allow the children to ask questions about how the items work. With small groups of children, show them how to turn the items in the collection on and off safely. Be aware of your school's policy on which items the children are allowed to turn on and off independently. It may be that you want to reinforce the message that switches operate these items, but that the children should never touch any switch without an adult. In any case, the children must not operate the switch by a wall socket. Explain that the danger arises because the items work by using electricity, which is dangerous. Many schools allow children to turn lights on and off, so teach safety procedures for doing this if appropriate. Explain the necessary rules to the children: making sure their hands are dry, taking turns to touch a switch rather than reaching for it together, and so on.
Differentiation	Talk with more able children about the other buttons on a cassette recorder, and explain that these are switches too: they allow the electricity through to make different things happen (winding or rewinding the tape, recording and so on). Less able children, and others, may need to be told not to operate any of the items unless an adult is with them and says it is safe to do so.
Assessment	Assess the children's understanding by asking them to draw pictures showing the rules you have talked about. Ask them to write (either independently or with an adult as scribe) a short sentence explaining the rules for the use of switches and electrical items in the classroom.
Plenary	Talk about the children's pictures and read some of their sentences to reinforce the message about not touching electrical appliances or to detail those appliances that the children are allowed to turn on and off independently. Add stickers with 'Yes' and 'No' (or a tick and a cross) to each appliance to show whether the children are allowed to touch it.
Outcomes	● Know that switches allow electricity through to make things work. ● Know which switches are safe to touch and which should never be touched. ● Can ask questions about how things work.

OBJECTIVE

● To learn that a range of household appliances use electricity.

RESOURCES

Main teaching activity: A soft toy; four large cardboard boxes, carpet squares; models of household furniture and electrical appliances found in different rooms (pictures cut from magazines and stuck to small cereal boxes are cheap alternatives).
Group activities: 1. Magazines and catalogues with pictures of electrical items, copies of photocopiable pages 130 and 131, sorting rings, labels. **2.** Pictures from Group activity 1, scissors, adhesive sticks, small cardboard boxes (such as toothpaste and cereal boxes). **3.** The 'home' role-play area. **4.** Paper, paints.

Vocabulary

kitchen, lounge, bedroom, dining room, electricity, electrical; the names of the appliances in your collection

PREPARATION

Make a doll's house with four rooms from cardboard boxes (all the same size) that the children will be able to reach into easily. Alternatively, create a model of four rooms with corrugated card strips, so that each room is approximately 50cm long, 50cm wide and 25cm high. Line the rooms with carpet squares or another suitable floor covering.

INTRODUCTION

Sit the children in a circle. Ask them to pass a soft toy around the circle. As each child takes the toy, he or she has to name an item in his or her home. (If the child does not wish to contribute, he or she can just pass the toy to the next person.) Ask questions such as: *Which item do you like the best in your bedroom? Why do you like this one the best?* Talk about all the things the children have mentioned that work by electricity. Explain that these are things that work when plugged into a wall socket and switched on, or when given batteries and switched on. As the children mention the names of electrical items in your collection of models, place these in the centre of the circle so that all the children can see them. Say that all the things in this new collection have something in common. After allowing the children to guess what (there are several things that the items may have in common), explain that the one you want them to learn is that the items all work by using electricity.

MAIN TEACHING ACTIVITY

Gather the children around your cardboard model of four rooms and tell them the names of the rooms that they represent. Choose one of the electrical items from the collection and invite the children to say in which room in the house it is found. Invite the children in turn to choose an item and place it in the room in which they think it belongs (for all or most of the time). Continue until all the items have been placed in the correct room. You may need to have more than one model of certain items, such as televisions and lamps.

GROUP ACTIVITIES

1. Work with groups of six children at a time to cut pictures of electrical items from magazines and catalogues and/or photocopiable pages 130 and 131, sorting them into sets according to the rooms in which the items are generally found. You may need more than one copy of some pictures (such as lamps and televisions).
2. Ask an adult helper to supervise the children while they stick the pictures from Group activity 1 onto small cardboard boxes and put them into the correct rooms in the model house.
3. Allow two children at a time to play with the doll's house, and four to play in the role-play area.
4. Ask the children to paint pictures of things in the house that work by electricity and things that do not. The latter could work by another power source (such as a gas fire) or not 'work' at all (such as a table).

DIFFERENTIATION

Ask more able children to identify the components on the appliances that show that they work by electricity, such as the plug, lead and switch. You may wish to ask them to identify these on photocopiable pages 130 and 131. This group could also consider appliances that use different sources of power, such as gas, oil or a winding mechanism.

With less able children, examine real small appliances such as a toaster, hairdryer, iron and kettle. Point out the lead and plug, which show that the appliance works by electricity. Reinforce the safety rules at the same time.

ASSESSMENT

Talk to the children about their paintings to find out who has or does not have an understanding of which things work by electricity.

PLENARY

Use the children's paintings to make a large wall display, inviting the children to say which half of the display each item belongs in (see illustration below). Ask the group making the model items to show what they have made and to identify which items work by electricity.

OUTCOMES

- Know that certain household appliances work by electricity.
- Can sort appliances according to the room they are usually found in.
- Can identify some household items that do not work by electricity.

LINKS

This lesson links with other aspects of knowledge and understanding of the world through the development of design and technology skills associated with joining and assembling materials.

LESSON 4

Objective	● To learn that electrical items may produce heat, sound, light and/or movement.
Resources	Magazines and catalogues with pictures of electrical items including washing machines, lamps, radios, cassette recorders, cookers, microwave ovens, heaters, fans, computers and TV sets; scissors, photocopiable page 132 (perhaps enlarged to A3 size), sorting rings; a collection of portable electrical items; the 'home' role-play area, labels, a felt-tipped pen.
Main activity	Show the children the pictures of electrical appliances in your collection. Talk about what each one is used for. Sort the pictures into rows according to whether each appliance gives heat, sound or light. Talk about the ones that also have a moving part, such as the drum in a washing machine or the blades on a fan. Organise Group activities with adult support: **1.** Work with groups of up to six children to cut out pictures of electrical items from magazines and catalogues, and/or from a copy of page 132, and talk about them. As the children cut out each picture, ask them why and how the appliance is used. *Does it gives out light, sound or heat? Does it have a moving part?* You may wish to sort the pictures into sets according to these properties. You may need to have more than one picture of some items that fit into more than one set (for example, a television gives out light and sound). More able children may cope with the concept of overlapping sets. **2.** Ask an adult helper to sort a collection of electrical appliances with groups of four children at a time. Use portable appliances such as a kettle, hairdryer, food mixer, lamp, portable CD player, cassette recorder, radio, iron and toaster. **3.** Ask four children to take it in turns to iron the doll's clothes, prepare a meal and listen to a taped story in the 'home' role-play area. Encourage them to think about how they are using electricity. **4.** With a group of children, label the play 'electric' items in the 'home' role play area according to whether they give out light, sound, heat or none of these.
Differentiation	In Group activity 1, talk with more able children about things that have motors: washing machines, tumble dryers, hairdryers and so on. Point out that these have parts that move. This will lead to some discussion about which set to place the pictures in, as all of these appliances have moving parts and also give out heat. Asking whether items with a motor also give out sound will lead to discussion of the sounds it gives out! A microwave oven is an interesting item to talk about, as it produces light, heat, sound and movement. Challenge the children to find other items that do this. Play 'Pick up a picture' with less able children, challenging them to find a picture of something that provides light, heat or sound. As their understanding develops, ask them to find a picture of something that gives out light *and* heat, light *and* sound and so on.
Assessment	Record the children's responses to your questions in Group activity 1, and note those who will need further support. How many children can find the appliances that have moving parts? Ask different ability groups to draw different numbers of items that give out heat, sound or light or make things move; keep the drawings as evidence of their understanding.
Plenary	Ask the more able group to talk about the items in the collection that have motors, explaining that these items all work with electricity and pointing out the bits that move.
Outcomes	● Know that electrical items can give out heat, light, sound and/or movement. ● Can sort objects according to given criteria. ● Can make drawings to record what they have found out.

Context: THE TOY SHOP

You may wish to keep this as part of a topic on 'My home', but it fits equally well into a topic on 'Toys'. Set up a toy shop in the role-play area and use its resources as a starting point for the next two lessons.

LESSON 5

OBJECTIVES
● To learn that a battery is a portable supply of electricity.
● To learn that some toys and other items are powered by batteries.

RESOURCES

Main teaching activity: A collection of batteries of different types and sizes; a camera; a collection of toys and other items that work by battery, including a talking bear or doll, a watch, a pottery wheel, a baby's musical mobile, a torch, a moving toy car.
Group activities: 1. Paper, pencils. **2.** Magazines or catalogues with pictures of battery-operated toys; photocopiable page 133, pencils. **3.** Paper, paints. **4.** A few battery-operated classroom objects (such as a radio, torch, calculator, clock, stopwatch and personal stereo).

Vocabulary

not safe, move, work, battery

PREPARATION

Test the things in your collection to make sure that they all work. Have spare batteries to hand.

INTRODUCTION

Organise the children so that they are sitting in a circle. Place the batteries in front of you. Ask the children if they know what these are called. Confirm that they are all 'batteries'. Ask the children whether they know what these are used for. Confirm that they are used to make things work. Explain that a battery contains a kind of electricity that is safe for us to use – but emphasise that batteries are not toys and should not be played with. We must take care with batteries in the same way that we take care with electricity. Explain that batteries usually contain a substance called 'acid' that is poisonous and can be very nasty when touched. It is safe to use battery-operated toys as long as we do not touch the battery. We must certainly never try to find out what is inside it. If we find a leaking battery, we must always tell an adult straight away.

MAIN TEACHING ACTIVITY

Invite the children to smile at this point, and take photographs of them all. Did they notice the flash? Ask whether they know what made the camera flash. You will get lots of answers to this question: the button, the bulb, the flash and so on. Explain that you had to press the button for the camera to work and that the bulb was what lit up, but that a battery inside the camera is providing the power to make the bulb light up. Without the battery, the flash would not work.

Look at the other things in your collection and talk about how the battery causes each item to work. Discuss whether the battery makes the item produce a sound, a light or a movement.

GROUP ACTIVITIES

1. Work with groups of six children to explore the range of items in the collection. Look inside each item to find the battery or batteries, and point these out to the children. Ask them to choose one of the toys and draw it with the battery compartment open, showing where the batteries are.
2. Ask an adult helper to work with groups of four children, cutting out pictures of battery-operated toys from catalogues and magazines. Each group should then work together to complete photocopiable page 133 by sorting the pictures into things that are battery-operated and things that are not. Check that the children are familiar with Scalextric sets.
3. Set up a painting table and ask the children to take it in turns to paint a picture of their favourite battery-operated toy.
4. Ask the children to find all the things in the classroom that are operated by battery. Make sure you have left one or two objects around for them to find, but also remember to remove things that you do not want them to touch (such as the video remote control).
5. Give less able children the opportunity to play with a selection of battery-operated toys.

DIFFERENTIATION

Ask more able children to work in groups, sorting the battery-operated items according to whether the battery causes the item to produce light, sound or movement. You may wish to develop the children's early prediction skills by asking them to say what will happen when the item is switched on before they try it.

Less able children should be given the opportunity to play with a range of battery-operated toys before taking part in the other activities in this lesson.

ASSESSMENT

Photocopiable page 133 asks the children to identify items that are operated by batteries and items that contain no batteries. If completed independently, the sheet can be retained as evidence of the children's understanding. Make a note of the amount of help given to those children who required it.

PLENARY

Talk about the children's paintings of toys. Together, make a display of things that work by battery and things that do not, similar to the display in Lesson 3 of this unit.

OUTCOMES

- Can recognise batteries.
- Know that batteries are a source of power and that they make things work.
- Know that some things work by battery and others do not.
- Know that batteries can be dangerous if not handled properly.

LINKS

Across the curriculum: a link with personal, social and emotional development is made through the children considering how to keep themselves and others safe.

LESSON 6

Objective	● To learn that many battery-operated items have a switch to turn them on and off.
Resources	A range of battery-operated toys and other items. Make sure that the items all work, and that you have spare batteries if necessary.
Main activity	Help the children to identify the switches on all the items in your collection. Organise Group activities with adult support: **1.** Ask an adult helper to work with a group of four children at a time, investigating and exploring how a range of battery-operated toys and other items work. The children should try to find the on/off switch on each item. **2.** Allow the children to play with the items, so that they are familiar with using the switches to make the items start and stop working. **3.** Work with groups of six to eight children, drawing pictures of an individually chosen item and labelling the on/off switch.
Differentiation	More able children can work independently on Group activity 2 before making their drawings. They have no need to complete Group activity 1. Less able children should be allowed to play with the items for five minutes before being directed to do Group activities 1 and 3.
Assessment	Keep the children's pictures of their chosen item and note on each one whether the task was completed independently or with support.
Plenary	Ask two or three children to talk about their favourite item and explain how they made it work by using the on/off switch. Talk about how the switch worked: *Did you push it or slide it?*
Outcomes	● Can identify the switch on a battery-operated item. ● Know that a switch may be needed to make something work. ● Can record findings by making drawings. ● Can begin to describe the movement of familiar objects.

UNIT 5 ELECTRICITY

LESSON 7

OBJECTIVES

● To assess the children's ability to identify and sort items by whether mains electricity or batteries power them.
● To assess the children's understanding of the dangers of electricity.

RESOURCES

Main activity: A collection of small electrical items, both mains-operated and battery-operated.
Assessment activities: 2. Photocopiable page 133, pencils. **3.** A set of pictures of items that work by mains electricity, by battery and by neither (the latter items might work by springs, hand force, solar power and so on); sorting rings.

PREPARATION

Make sure that the electrical items in the collection work. Make one copy for each child of photocopiable page 133.

MAIN ASSESSMENT ACTIVITY

Look at the things in your collection. Show the children how the mains-operated items work before letting them play with the battery-operated items. Spend a few minutes talking about how the items work before sorting them together into two sets: those operated by mains electricity and those operated by battery. Find out by questioning which children understand that electricity is dangerous.

ASSESSMENT ACTIVITY 2

Ask the children to complete photocopiable page 133, which asks them to identify items powered by mains electricity or by battery.

ASSESSMENT ACTIVITY 3

Work with groups of four children to sort a set of pictures (different from those on page 133) into items that work by electricity, items that work by battery and items that use neither.

Assessment outcomes

On completion of these Assessment activities, you should know which children have attained the following objectives linked to knowledge and understanding of the world:
● Know that some things work by mains electricity, some work by battery and some use neither.
● Identify whether a range of familiar objects work by battery or by mains electricity.
● Know that electricity can be dangerous.

PLENARY

Look at the set of pictures used in Assessment activity 3, with a few additional ones, and sort these together into two sets: those appliances powered by mains electricity and those powered by a battery.

Do not touch!

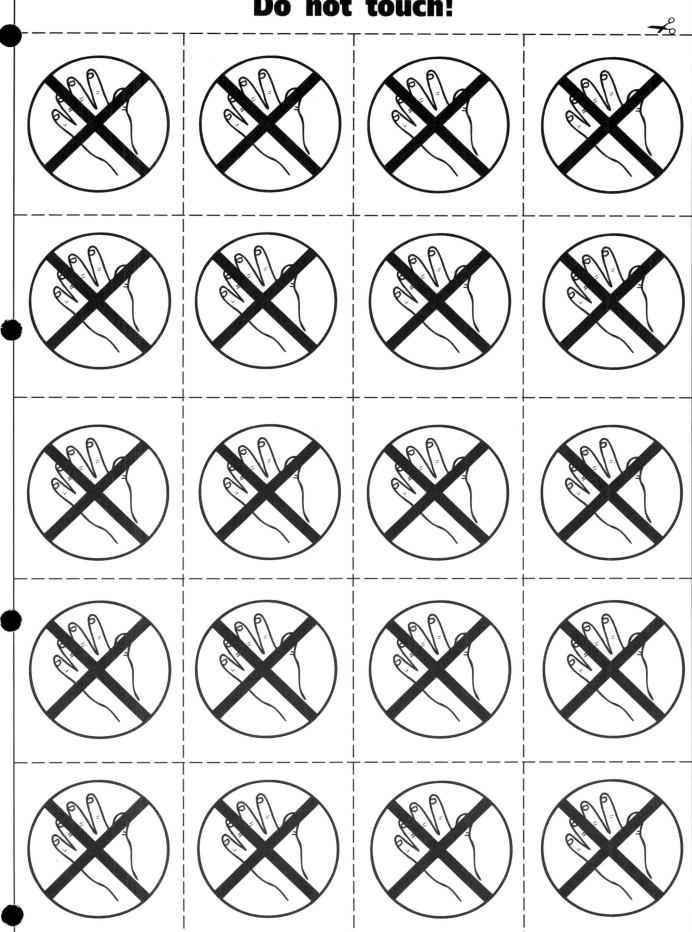

Things that use electricity 1

UNIT 5 ELECTRICITY

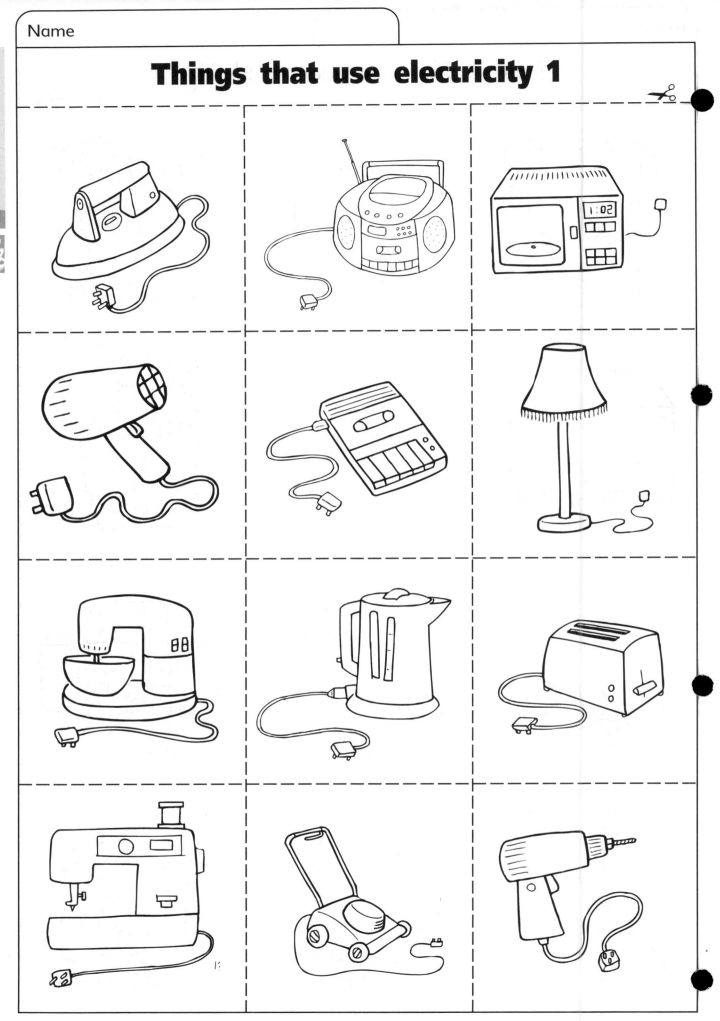

Name

Things that use electricity 2

Name

What does it do?

How does it work?

Name

In the box by each picture, write **b** if it works by battery and **m** if it works by mains electricity.

Pushing and pulling

ORGANISATION (10 LESSONS)

	OBJECTIVES	MAIN ACTIVITY	GROUP ACTIVITIES	PLENARY	OUTCOMES
LESSON 1	● To learn that string, rope, laces, cords and other non-rigid items must be pulled and not pushed.	Pull and push a skipping rope. Talk about things that use a cord or string. Make pulley systems. Explore the effects of pulling and pushing strings and laces.		Ask children to demonstrate and explain their pulleys and pull-along toys.	● Know some uses of rope, string and cord. ● Know that rope, string and cord are pulled, not pushed, when they are used. ● Know that it is sometimes easier to lift things with pulleys than to lift them by hand.
LESSON 2	● To discover that we need to pull (not push) most of our clothes on when we get dressed.	Explore how we pull items of clothing on and off.	Play the 'Dress the teddy' computer game and a 'Dress the bear' board game. Use dressing-up to explore how clothes are pulled on. Make a bed.	Invite an adult to put on a sari or turban.	● Know that most items of clothing are put on with a pull. ● Can make drawings to record what they have found out. ● Can identify simple things that certain items have in common.
LESSON 3	● To learn that some toys move when pushed, some when pulled and others when either pushed or pulled. ● To begin to sort objects according to the way they are moved, and to record the results by drawing.	Explore a collection of toys that work with a push, with a pull or with either. Draw the toys.	Investigate the movement of a rocking horse. Ride tricycles and see-saws. Develop bat and ball skills. Role-play a toyshop.	Talk about how the children made the tricycles move. Sort the children's drawings.	● Know that some toys work by being pushed, some by being pulled and some by being either pushed or pulled. ● Can investigate the movement of familiar things. ● Can make drawings to record the results of an investigation. ● Can talk about what they have found out.
LESSON 4	● To explore how a range of familiar objects can be moved by pulling.	Talk about what things are pulled in the story of 'The Enormous Turnip'. Make string patterns. Pull cards from envelopes.		Label items in the classroom that operate by a pull.	● Know that some things move when pulled. ● Can draw pictures to record their findings.
LESSON 5	● To explore a range of objects that move or work by being pushed.	Push a wheelbarrow and talk about its movement.	Explore finger painting. Make Ice cakes. Make symmetrical blob patterns. Blow paint through a straw. Push vehicles on a track.	Talk about how the straw-blown paintings and symmetrical patterns were made.	● Explore and identify a range of things that move when pushed. ● Can explain how they used their fingers and air to push paint around paper. ● Can explain how they used their fingers to push icing out of a bag or tube.
LESSON 6	● To learn that when air is pushed into a balloon, the balloon stretches and changes shape.	Teach vocabulary to describe how a balloon changes size and shape as it is inflated.	Watch balloon models being made. Inflate balloons. Keep a balloon in the air. Investigate how designs on balloons change as they are inflated.	Demonstrate and talk about how balloon models are made.	● Understand that when air is pushed into it, a balloon gets bigger and changes shape. ● Can record changes by drawing 'Before' and 'After' pictures. ● Can recognise familiar objects that can be made bigger by pushing air into them.

ORGANISATION (10 LESSONS)

	OBJECTIVES	MAIN ACTIVITY	GROUP ACTIVITIES	PLENARY	OUTCOMES
LESSON 7	● To learn that when a push is applied to an object, it may move.	Demonstrate how to make a stick puppet. Talk about how it works.	Make stick puppets. Create a puppet play. Order pictures to record the process of making the puppets.	The children perform their puppet plays. Discuss how the puppets work.	● Know that a push can make something move. ● Have begun to understand that a pushing force is opposite to a pulling force. ● Can show what they did by putting pictures into a sequence.
LESSON 8	● To learn that pushing can change the position and shape of some objects.	Perform bending actions. Make pipe-cleaner sculptures, pipe-cleaner puppets and wire sculptures. Explore a range of 'bendy' materials.		The children demonstrate how their puppets can be bent into new shapes and positions.	● Know that some materials will bend when pushed. ● Know that some things can change shape and position. ● Can select from a range of materials to make models and sculptures.
LESSON 9	● To investigate how pushing or pulling a stick can make something move.	Look at books that have moveable parts. Make cards and a display with parts that move. Make puppet theatres.		The children talk about the things they have made, explaining how the parts that move work.	● Know that sticks can make things move. ● Know that a push or a pull can make something move. ● Can persevere to produce a model with moving parts.

	OBJECTIVES	MAIN ACTIVITY	ACTIVITIES 2 and 3	ACTIVITY 4	OUTCOMES
ASSESSMENT 10	● To assess the children's ability to identify whether items need a push, a pull, either or both to make them work.	Sort a collection of fasteners by how they work.	Sort various other items in a similar way. Identify objects that need a pull, a push or either to work.	Find objects in the classroom that need a pull, a push or either to work.	● Can say whether familiar objects require a pull, a push or either to make them work. ● Know that the fasteners on our clothes need to be pushed, pulled or pushed and pulled to open and close them. ● Can sort familiar objects into three sets according to given criteria.

Context: THE TOY SHOP/RHYMES

This lesson can be set in the context of a toy shop (see Lessons 3–9) or a 'Stories and rhymes' topic. For example, it could follow up a literacy activity looking at rhyming words.

LESSON 1

Objective	● To learn that string, rope, laces, cords and other non-rigid items must be pulled and not pushed.
Resources	A skipping rope; a length of string, curtain cord or blind cord; the classroom window-blind; a collection of pull-along toys; short pieces of string; an old shoe and shoelace. Make a display of 'Hickory Dickory Dock' and 'Little Miss Muffet', with text, pictures and models of a spider and a mouse. For extension: a model car with a trailer attached loosely by a shoelace.
Main activity	Have a ten-minute skipping session with the children, talking about how the skipping rope bends and curls. *Can you keep it straight?* Tell them that they can only keep it straight by pulling it out tight.
	Sit the children in a circle and arrange the skipping rope as a smaller circle in front of them. Challenge them to push the rope away from them. Repeat the activity with a length of string or cord. Talk about how items such as string and rope cannot easily be pushed somewhere, because they are bendy and not stiff or rigid. Show the children how the blind in the classroom works. Encourage them to think of other things that work by a length of cord or string being pulled, such as pulleys, 'up and over' garage doors and curtains. Organise Group activities with adult support:
	1. Ask an adult helper to work with groups of up to eight children, making a pulley system to help the mouse go up the clock and the spider fall next to Miss Muffet. Emphasise that in the latter case, the cord is used to pull the spider up to the top. Each time the cord is pulled, the mouse and spider both go up. Ask more able children to explain this as they make the pull.
	2. Make a pulley system outside for groups of four children to use – for example, to pull buckets of sand to the top of a table from the ground. Invite the children to explain what they are doing.
	3. Allow a group of six children to play with a range of pull-along toys. Challenge them to push the toys using only the string.
	4. Attach string to some of the toys in the classroom for groups of up to six children to pull along.
	5. Work with groups of six children on lacing a shoe; talk about threading and pulling. Discuss the reason why the end of the lace has a hard bit. Challenge the children to push the lace all the way through the holes until it is tight. Does anyone manage it? If anyone says they can, ask them to show you!
Differentiation	Introduce the term 'towing' with more able children, and investigate situations where ropes are used for pulling – for example, to lead animals. Ask them to record all the situations they can think of. Talk about why a rope is not used for towing a caravan. Use a model to demonstrate that when the car stops, a trailer on a rope will crash into it. Organise the less able children in pairs, with one rope between them. Ask them to pull the rope out straight. Explore what you mean by 'tight', 'rigid' and 'straight'. Now challenge them to push the rope. Explore what you mean by 'slack' and 'bendy'.
Assessment	Note those children who have a good understanding of what a pull is. Note those who can describe how a rope can be pulled to make it straight, but cannot be pushed. Ask the children to name other things around the classroom that can be pulled but not pushed, and note those who are able to do so.
Plenary	Ask the children who have been playing with the pull-along toys to demonstrate how they have to pull these toys to make them move. Ask a group who raised buckets of sand to explain how they got them to the top of the table without straining their backs. Point out that the string in the pulley was used to pull, not push.
Outcomes	● Know some uses of rope, string and cord. ● Know that rope, string and cord are pulled, not pushed, when they are used. ● Know that it is sometimes easier to lift things with pulleys than to lift them by hand.

Context: TAKING CARE OF MYSELF

Teaching the children to take care of themselves is a good topic to base the following lesson in. The lesson focuses on the children's dressing and undressing skills.

LESSON 2

OBJECTIVE
● To discover that we need to pull (not push) most of our clothes on when we get dressed.

RESOURCES

Main teaching activity: A copy of the song 'I Jump out of Bed in the Morning' from *Okki-tokki-unga* edited by Beatrice Harrop (A&C Black); paper, pencils; the children in shoes and socks.
Group activities: 1. The *My World* 'Dress the teddy' program from Semerc, photocopiable page 148, coloured pencils. **2.** Socks, Wellington boots, a hat, mittens, a jumper, trousers and sunglasses to fit four teddy bears or dolls; a spinner and board (see Preparation). **4.** Dressing-up clothes, four PE hoops. **5.** A toy bed with bedclothes.
Plenary: An adult visitor dressed in a sari or a turban.

Vocabulary
pull, socks, boots, hat, mittens, jumper, trousers, sunglasses, sari, turban

PREPARATION

Make a board with a spinner and pictures of the types of dressing-up clothes in your collection (see illustration overleaf). Send a letter to parents or carers, asking for clothes to fit the teddy bears or dolls.

INTRODUCTION

Sing the song 'I Jump out of Bed in the Morning', adding verses for getting dressed such as 'I pull on my socks in the morning'. Draw pictures of all the items that the children suggest that they have to pull on when they get dressed.

MAIN TEACHING ACTIVITY

Ask the children to pull off their shoes. Now ask them to pull off their socks. Organise them into pairs and challenge them to push each other's socks back onto their feet. *Who can do this?* If anyone says they can, ask them to show everyone so that you can all copy! Explain that we always pull our socks off, and we have to pull them on also. You may need to tell them that the only thing pushing is their feet, not the socks and shoes. Link this to Lesson 1 if you wish. Ask the children to think of other items of clothing that always have to be pulled on and off. Add these to your collection of drawings.

GROUP ACTIVITIES

1. Ask an adult helper to play the computer game 'Dress the teddy' with pairs of children. He or she should talk about all the items that the teddy has had to pull on as he gets dressed, then print the screen (or use photocopiable page 148) and ask the children to colour each item that needs to be pulled on.

2. Play a 'Dress the bear' board game with four children at a time. They should take turns to spin the arrow: when it stops on an item of clothing, the child whose turn it is can find that item and put it on his or her teddy bear. If the bear is already wearing the item, the child has to wait for his or her next turn. The clothes cannot be put on in the wrong order (for example, boots before socks or boots before trousers). The first child to dress his or her bear completely is the winner.

3. Set up a dressing-up race outside (or indoors if it is cold): the children have to run through a sequence of four hoops, each containing a type of clothing, and put on one of each item. The first child to become fully dressed is the winner. Afterwards, ask the children to draw all the clothes they pulled on.

4. Play with the dressing-up clothes in an area of the classroom, occasionally asking the children which items of clothing they put on by pulling, asking them to draw these and adding them to the collection of drawings.

5. Set up a toy bed in one corner of the classroom. (You could relate this to the story of the Three Bears, reminding the children that Goldilocks took Baby Bear's bed as well as his porridge.) Ask the children to work in pairs to make the bed by pulling on the pillowcases, pulling the sheets over the mattress and pulling the duvet or blankets straight. Make a display of 'Making a bed', writing instructions for the children to follow with the word 'pull' underlined.

DIFFERENTIATION

Reinforce the learning objective with less able children every time they get dressed and undressed for PE, until you are sure that they understand the meaning of 'pull'.

Ask more able children to find other items around the classroom that have to be pulled and not pushed, for example putting the cover on a beanbag or cushion, straightening a rug or other fabric item. *Can you see anything that they have in common?* (They all involve thin fabric.)

ASSESSMENT

In Group activity 3, ask the children to draw their own pictures of clothes that are put on by pulling. Note which children are able to think of additional clothes to the ones used in the lesson.

PLENARY

Ask an adult to show the children how a sari or a turban is put on. Both items require lots of pulling around the body or the head, and are fascinating to watch.

OUTCOMES

- Know that most items of clothing are put on with a pull.
- Can make drawings to record what they have found out.
- Can identify simple things that certain items have in common.

LINKS

Across the curriculum: this lesson also develops physical skills, personal skills of dressing and social skills of taking turns and playing fairly.

Context: THE TOY SHOP

The context of the next seven lessons is the toy shop. For this, you can use a range of toys already in the classroom and any that you have used to set up the role-play area. These resources can be used in all of the lessons to investigate pushing and pulling. Choose some toys from the outset that only need a push to work, some that only need a pull and some that need either a pull or a push (see Lesson 3 below).

LESSON 3

OBJECTIVES

● To learn that some toys move when pushed, some when pulled and others when either pushed or pulled.
● To begin to sort objects according to the way they are moved, and to record the results by drawing.

RESOURCES

Main teaching activity: A collection of things found in a toy shop that can be pulled and/or pushed, including a toy piano, a talking toy with a pull cord, a talking book with buttons to operate its sound effects, a variety of push and pull toys, Lego bricks and other construction kits; labels marked 'Push', 'Pull' and 'Push and pull'.
Group activities: 1. A rocking horse. **2.** A tricycle, a pram, a pushchair, a 'sit and ride' toy, a see-saw. **3.** Bats and balls. **4.** The 'toy shop' role-play area.
Plenary: A large sheet of paper, a felt-tipped pen.

Vocabulary

pull, push, open, close, in, out, forwards, backwards, to and fro

PREPARATION

Set up a tricycle track outside. Organise an adult helper to direct the learning of the group playing with the bats and balls, while you supervise the other groups.

INTRODUCTION

Allow the children some time to play with the toys in the collection, either at the beginning of the lesson or during a previous play activity. This will ensure that they are able to talk about them from first-hand experience of their movements, knowing whether they need a push, a pull or both to be operated.

MAIN TEACHING ACTIVITY

Play a tune that the children will recognise on a toy piano. Ask the children what you are doing to make the piano work. Explain that you are *pushing* the keys down, and this makes the piano play the notes. Now pick up the talking book and show the children how the sound effects are operated when you push the buttons. Emphasise that these two toys work when something is *pushed*. Put them together to one side.

Pick up a toy that talks and pull its cord. Listen as it talks, and watch the cord returning to its starting place. Invite one of the children to say what you did to make the toy talk. He or she should say that you pulled the cord. Select another toy from the collection that requires a pull to make it work. Put these two toys together in another place.

Repeat the activity with two toys that need either a pull or a push to operate them, such as building bricks or a pram. Put these into a third place together. Label the three groups.

Ask an adult helper to supervise groups of six children as they talk about the three groups in turn, adding other toys from the collection and recording by drawing pictures.

GROUP ACTIVITIES

1. Work with a group of four children, investigating the movement of a rocking horse. Let each child have a turn at riding the horse while the others watch. Afterwards, talk about how the horse was made to rock forwards and backwards. Show the children how that works by using your hand to rock the horse: first pushing on the front of the horse to make it go forwards, then pushing on its back to make it go backwards. Explain what is happening as you do so. Reinforce the children's understanding that they push forwards and then backwards to make the horse rock by letting each child have another turn, feeling the different pushes as the horse rocks.

2. Set up a tricycle track outside and allow the children to ride around it. Use any other wheeled toys you have for the children to play with, including prams, pushchairs and 'sit and ride' toys. You may also have a see-saw for the children to explore. All of these require a push to move, and the children should be able to feel this as they push with their legs.

3. Ask an adult helper to work with groups of six to eight children, playing outside with bats and balls. As they throw, catch and hit the balls, the helper should talk about how they are pushing a

ball through the air with their hands or a bat, making the ball go forwards and/or upwards.
4. Allow a group of four children to buy and sell toys in the 'toy shop' role-play area.

DIFFERENTIATION

Set up a skittle game for more able children to play. Talk about how the ball pushes
the skittles over. Which children are able to say that they are pushing the ball, which is
pushing the skittles over?

Allow less able children to push cars around a play mat. Talk about what they are doing,
without relating the push to the movement of the car. Give them pull-along toys to play with,
and tell them that they are pulling the toy along. It is appropriate for them to learn only what is
meant by a push and a pull; if they are ready, go on to relate this to the movement of the toy.
Use this activity as an assessment with this group.

ASSESSMENT

Keep one or two additional toys to one side. At the end of Group activity 1, ask the children to
say whether each of these items needs a push, a pull or either to work.

PLENARY

Ask a group who were riding tricycles and playing with wheeled toys to talk about what they
were doing. Ask a child to explain how he or she made the tricycle move. Many will tell you that
they 'pedalled' or 'rode' it, but some may say that they 'pushed the pedals round'. Emphasise or
provide this explanation of how the tricycle works. Together, make three sets of drawings: toys
that need a push to work, toys that need a pull and toys that need either.

OUTCOMES

● Know that some toys work by being pushed, some by being pulled and some by
being either pushed or pulled.
● Can investigate the movement of familiar things.
● Can make drawings to record the results of an investigation.
● Can talk about what they have found out.

LINKS

Between units: this lesson links with Unit 4, Lesson 8, where the pushing force of rolling out
dough to make biscuits is discussed.
Across the curriculum: this lesson provides opportunities to develop speaking skills by talking
about what they are doing, and to develop gross motor and hand-eye co-ordination skills while
using the various toys.

LESSON 4

Objective	● To explore how a range of familiar objects can be moved by pulling.
Resources	A version of *The Enormous Turnip*; a collection of vegetables (including a carrot, parsnip, potato, onion, cauliflower, sprout and cabbage); paper, string, paint in a variety of colours; envelopes, cards (some of which say 'You have won a prize. Well done!'), a sheet of pictorial stickers; Post-it notes.
Main activity	Read *The Enormous Turnip*, a traditional tale, and talk about all the people who had to pull up the turnip. Talk about the other vegetables that are pulled out of the ground. You may wish to say at this point that weeds can be pulled up, but wild flowers should never be. Show your collection of vegetables and ask the children to draw a pictorial list of all the things that are pulled up. Refer back to Lessons 2 and 3 in this unit to talk about pulling and pushing different objects. Organise Group activities with adult support: **1.** Make string patterns with the children and talk about how they are pulling the string to make a pattern. **2.** Play a game in which the children pull a card from an envelope to find out whether they have won a prize. The prizes are stickers that require pulling from a sheet. **3.** Play the 'Dress the bear' game from Lesson 2 of this unit again.
Differentiation	Allow more able children to go on a 'pulling safari', using a display of objects that only work or move when pulled (such as blinds, curtains and tape measures). Give less able children plenty of opportunities to explore at length the range of items that work by pulling, and to talk to adults about what is happening.
Assessment	Ask the children to draw pictures of all the things that they pulled during the Group activities. Note those children who include things that they pushed, and repeat some activities to reinforce their understanding of pushes and pulls.
Plenary	Ask the children to identify all the things in the classroom that need to be pulled. Invite some children to label these, using Post-it notes with the word 'Pull' written on.
Outcomes	● Know that some things move when pulled. ● Can draw pictures to record their findings.

LESSON 5

OBJECTIVE
● To explore a range of objects that move or work by being pushed.

RESOURCES
Main teaching activity: A wheelbarrow.
Group activities: 1. Tubes of thick paint, paper. **2.** Icing in an icing bag, cakes. **3.** Thick paint, paper. **4.** Straws, paints in a range of colours, paper. **5.** A collection of wheeled toys.

Vocabulary

topple, balance, squeeze, push out

MAIN TEACHING ACTIVITY
Look at a wheelbarrow together and discuss how we can make it work. Talk about the wheel and how important it is to keep the wheelbarrow balanced, as it can easily topple over. Ask: *Do you pull or push the wheelbarrow? Can you do both?* Explain that it is possible to do both, but we usually push the barrow because we can steer it better and can watch to make sure that it stays balanced. Demonstrate this to the children.

GROUP ACTIVITIES
1. Work with groups of four children to explore finger painting. Let the children push thick paint from a tube or plastic bottle by squeezing, then swirl the paint around by pushing it with their fingers into recognisable shapes, letters and numbers or into imaginative drawings and patterns. Finally, while the painting is still wet, they should make a print of it.
2. Ask an adult helper to work with groups of four children, using icing bags to ice cakes. This requires the children to push the icing out with their fingers. They can use different-patterned ends to create different shapes and patterns.
3. Let the children work independently to make symmetrical patterns by blobbing paint into the centre of a sheet of paper, then folding the sheet and pushing the paint outwards and around between the sides.
4. Let the children make pictures and patterns in several colours by blowing air onto paint with straws, so the paint moves across the paper. Make sure that they don't get paint in the straws.
5. Set up a trail outside for the children to push toy wheelbarrows, prams, pushchairs and shopping trolleys around.

DIFFERENTIATION

Give less able children plenty of opportunities to play with a range of toys and objects that need a push. Make sure that they receive adult intervention to challenge their thinking, and that they talk about the pushes they are exerting on the objects to make something move.

Ask more able children to go on a 'pushing safari' and label all the things they can find that require a push to make them move or work: a light switch, a door handle, a doorbell, a computer keyboard and so on.

ASSESSMENT

Ask the children to draw a picture of their favourite activity and to label the pushing action in the correct place. Note those children who are able to do this unaided. (Also see Plenary.)

PLENARY

Ask the children to talk about how they made their straw-blowing and symmetrical pictures and patterns. This will allow you to check on the success of these activities and to assess the children's understanding of how they pushed the paint by blowing or using their fingers.

OUTCOMES

● Explore and identify a range of things that move when pushed.
● Can explain how they used their fingers and air to push paint around paper.
● Can explain how they used their fingers to push icing out of a bag or tube.

LINKS

Across the curriculum: some of the activities in this lesson can be used to develop the children's creativity by giving them the freedom to create their own pictures and patterns. The control they need to exercise when icing the cakes supports the development of their fine motor co-ordination skills.

LESSON 6

OBJECTIVE

● To learn that when air is pushed into a balloon, the balloon stretches and changes shape.

RESOURCES

Main teaching activity: Balloons, a balloon pump.
Group activities: 1. Thin balloons that can be 'sculpted' into models (modelling balloons can be bought specifically for this purpose). **2–5.** Balloons in different shapes and sizes, including some with pictures, words and numbers printed on them. **5.** Paints or marker pens.

Vocabulary

grow, bigger, air, blow up, inflate, round, long, stretch, bounce, float, thinner, change shape

PREPARATION

Find an adult helper who can make animals and other models from thin balloons.

INTRODUCTION

Blow up a balloon until it is quite big, then release it for the children to watch what happens. As the balloon darts about the room, prepare another and release it. Talk about the pathways taken by the balloons.

MAIN TEACHING ACTIVITY

As you inflate a balloon, talk to the children about how the pump is pushing air into it. Emphasise the *pull* and *push* of the balloon pump. Ask one or two children to say what is happening to the balloon as the air is pushed in. Use words such as 'expanding', 'growing', 'stretching' and 'getting bigger'. Ask: *Is the balloon getting thinner? How do you know? Is the balloon changing shape? What will happen if air keeps on being pushed into the balloon?* Compare an inflated balloon with one that has no air.

GROUP ACTIVITIES

1. Ask an adult helper to come into the classroom and make balloon animals and other models. Ask him or her to talk about how the balloon is stretching and changing shape.
2. Ask the same adult to help individual children inflate a balloon using the balloon pump and add it to a balloon display. This could be a frame for a birthday graph or a display about a recent celebration.
3. Play a game in PE in which the children must keep a balloon in the air. Talk about how they need to push the balloon with their hands or feet to keep it up.
4. Work with a group of six children, observing what happens to printed numbers, pictures and words as a balloon is inflated. The children should draw 'Before' and 'After' pictures and write words to describe what the balloon looks like before and after it is inflated. Reinforce the vocabulary that describes how the balloon changes: *It stretches, expands, grows, gets bigger and changes shape as it is inflated.*
5. Ask the children to paint faces or write numbers on inflated balloons. Display the faces above labels with the children's names, or display the numbers in a line.

DIFFERENTIATION

Talk with the more able children about other things that can be inflated, such as balls, bouncy castles and space hoppers. Talk about the materials from which these things are made, and their properties. Inflate a ball and space hopper and invite the children to explain in turn what is happening as each one is inflated. Can they apply this to explain what is happening when a bouncy castle is inflated?

Make sure that the less able children take part in Group activities 2 and 4. Give them further opportunities to inflate a balloon, talking about how it changes in size.

ASSESSMENT

Use the 'Before' and 'After' pictures to assess whether children understand that a balloon gets bigger and changes shape when air is pushed into it. Ask more able children to write about, or draw pictures of, other things that get bigger and change shape when air is pushed into them.

PLENARY

Ask the adult helper to make balloon animals and models while the whole class watches. Talk about how the shape of the balloon is changing as it is twisted and turned, and how the air inside is pushing the rubber wall in different directions.

OUTCOMES

- Understand that when air is pushed into it, a balloon gets bigger and changes shape.
- Can record changes by drawing 'Before' and 'After' pictures.
- Can recognise familiar objects that can be made bigger by pushing air into them.

LINKS

Between units: this lesson links with Unit 4, and can be used as a context to talk about materials changing shape. More able children can explore the properties of elastic materials under careful adult supervision.

Context: PUPPET SHOW

The next three lessons are still set in the context of a toy shop, but they can also be taught as part of a topic on puppets.

LESSON 7

OBJECTIVE
● To learn that when a push is applied to an object, it may move.

RESOURCES

Main teaching activity: A copy of the song 'Dingle Dangle Scarecrow' from *This Little Puffin* compiled by Elizabeth Matterson (Puffin), a pop-up scarecrow puppet.
Group activities: 1. Photocopiable page 149, materials to make each puppet (a disposable plastic or card cup, a square of fabric approximately 20cm × 20cm, a length of dowelling approximately 20cm long, a circle of paper, a table-tennis or polystyrene ball, a strip of card 2cm wide and the same length as the diameter of the top of the cup); felt-tipped pens, adhesive tape, PVA glue, scissors. **3.** Dowelling, paper. **4.** Photocopiable page 150, scissors, glue, paper.

Vocabulary

pop up, push, move

PREPARATION

Make a large prototype scarecrow puppet (see instructions on page 149) and learn the rhyme.

INTRODUCTION

Sing 'Dingle Dangle Scarecrow'. At the appropriate time, make the puppet pop out of the cup.

MAIN TEACHING ACTIVITY

Show the children your puppet and talk about the things you used to make it. Demonstrate how you made the puppet, using the 'Blue Peter' method (*Here's one I made earlier...*). Make a list of the items used in the order that you used them, giving each one a number. Talk about how the puppet works. Show and tell the children that as you push the stick, the puppet appears out of the cup. Say: *The push makes the puppet move.*

GROUP ACTIVITIES

1. Working with groups of four children, give each child the necessary materials to make their own puppet and a copy of the instruction sheet (page 149). All the children should complete this activity. When they have finished, talk to them about how the puppet works. Ask them to draw their puppet and label it to show how it works.
2. Ask the groups, as they finish their pop-up puppets, to work with an adult helper, making up a short puppet play to show the other children in the class.
3. Allow children who are sufficiently able to work independently in groups of six, making their own stick puppets from dowelling and paper.
4. Give the children a copy each of page 150. Ask them to cut out the pictures and arrange them in the correct order, then stick them in place.

DIFFERENTIATION

Ask more able children what they should do to make the puppet go back into the cup. Note the ones who say that you can either pull it back down using the stick (especially if they say that they need to pull it back in because they pushed it out, thus showing awareness that a pulling force is the opposite of a pushing force) or push it back in from above.
   Less able children should be given time to play with their finished puppets before talking about how these move or work.

ASSESSMENT

Use the children's labelled drawings to assess their understanding of how the puppet works. Use their work with page 150 to assess their understanding of how the puppet is put together.

PLENARY

Ask the children to perform their puppet plays for each other. At the end, talk about how they made their puppets work.

OUTCOMES
● Know that a push can make something move.
● Have begun to understand that a pushing force is opposite to a pulling force.
● Can show what they did by putting pictures into a sequence.

LINKS

Across the curriculum: this activity links well with literacy work, as the children can be asked to develop their plays over a number of days. The plays can be used as a context for text-level work and/or guided writing. The children's speaking and listening skills will also be developed by this work.

LESSON 8

Objective	● To learn that pushing can change the position and shape of some objects.
Resources	Plastic-coated garden wire, pipe-cleaners, a tightly rolled sheet of paper, a simple coat or tunic (to dress a puppet), sticky tape, paper, felt-tipped pens, sharp scissors. Making a puppet beforehand will give you more confidence during the lesson, and will give you the opportunity to identify any likely pitfalls for the children.

Main activity	Play a game, using a rhyme to the tune of 'Here We Go Round the Mulberry Bush'. Sing: 'This is the way I bend my…' (bending a part of the body). Invite the children to stand up and do the actions.
	    Give each child a pipe-cleaner. Let the children play with these for a while before asking them to make an interesting shape or model. Give them another pipe-cleaner and ask them to attach it to the first. Let pairs look at each other's sculptures. Show the children how to twist the ends of pipe-cleaners together to make a join. Explain that pipe-cleaners are made from a material that can be pushed to bend it into different shapes. Look at some garden wire and repeat the activity.
	    Organise Group activities with adult support:
	1. Work with a group of six children to make a puppet. Use the pipe-cleaners and wire to make a body shape. Twist the pipe-cleaners into a circle to make the feet, and use five smaller pieces to make fingers. Dress the puppet in a simple tunic made from two squares of fabric. Draw features on a paper circle to make a face; attach it with adhesive tape. Ask the children to draw a picture of their puppet and use arrows to show the places where a human body would bend (elbows, waist, knees and neck).
	2. Ask an adult helper to supervise the children as they explore plastic-coated wire to make simple three-dimensional sculptures.
	3. Let the children explore a range of 'bendy' materials that can be pushed into different shapes: paper and plastic straws, sheets of paper, strips of cardboard. Let them select their own material to make sculptures. Provide adhesive tape for them to join their structures with.

Differentiation	Work with more able children, sorting the range of materials into groups: 'Will fold', 'Will not fold'; 'Will twist', 'Will not twist'; 'Will bend', 'Will not bend'. Include some materials that will do none of these things, such as wood. Allow less able children lots of time to explore and talk about how they are bending and twisting the materials to change their position and shape. Encourage them to use the appropriate vocabulary.
Assessment	From the children's pictures of their puppets, note those who have correctly indicated where the human body bends.
Plenary	Ask the children to show their puppets to the class and demonstrate how they bend and change position. Reinforce the learning objective: the puppets are being pushed into new positions and shapes.
Outcomes	● Know that some materials will bend when pushed. ● Know that some things can change shape and position. ● Can select from a range of materials to make models and sculptures.

LESSON 9

Objective	● To investigate how pushing or pulling a stick can make something move.
Resources	Some of the *Spot* books by Eric Hill (Picture Puffin); a large display area; lollipop sticks, paper circles, adhesive sticks; a variety of paper, fabric, card and sticks; cardboard boxes, scissors, paint, brushes. Cover the display board with paper and cut-out card in wavy shapes.
Main activity	Look at some books that use cardboard strips to make things move on the page and paper flaps to hide things, such as the *Spot* books by Eric Hill. Talk about how the things in the book move. Look closely at how a picture can be moved when it is stuck to the end of a cardboard strip or lollipop stick. Give each child a lollipop stick and a card circle or sticker to play with, and show how these can be moved about. Organise Group activities with adult support: **1.** Let the children make cards showing the nursery rhyme 'Hey Diddle Diddle', making the cow jump over the Moon by attaching a picture to the end of a lollipop stick. **2.** Let the children make cards decorated with flowers, with a slit across the middle at the bottom that starts and finishes about 2cm from either edge so that an animal can 'run' across the front of the card. **3.** Together, sponge-paint the wave shapes and staple them across the top of the display board. Design, paint and cut out fish shapes, attach them to strips of card and thread them through the waves, so that the children can make the fish move across the display. **4.** Help the children to make puppet theatres from cardboard boxes with slits cut in the back, top and sides. They should stick drawings of characters to lollipop sticks or card strips, thread these through the slits in the box and make them move. Let them perform their own puppet shows.
Differentiation	Some children will need a lot of help to assemble their models. If necessary, allow an adult helper to do the fiddly bits before you take over and talk to the children about how their finished model works.
Assessment	In the Plenary session, listen to check whether the children can describe how their model works.
Plenary	Let the children show the things that they have made. Ask them to say how each one works. How do they make the things move? Do they push or pull the sticks?
Outcomes	● Know that sticks can make things move. ● Know that a push or a pull can make something move. ● Can persevere to produce a model with moving parts.

ASSESSMENT

LESSON 10

OBJECTIVE

● To assess the children's ability to identify whether items need a push, a pull, either or both to make them move or work.

RESOURCES

Main assessment activity: A selection of clothes with zips, buttons, hook-and-eye and press-stud fastenings; a selection of shoes with Velcro fasteners, buckles and laces; three sorting rings labelled 'Push', 'Pull' and 'Push and pull'. **Assessment activities: 2.** A collection of objects used in Lessons 1–5. **3.** Three cards labelled as above. **4.** More sets of label cards (one card per child).

INTRODUCTION

Show the children the items of footwear and clothing and show them all the different fasteners. Ask each child, in turn, to show the others how one fastener works.

MAIN ASSESSMENT ACTIVITY

Talk to the children about the zip fastener. *Is the zip pulled or pushed to make it move up and down, or does it need to be pushed one way and pulled the other way?* Tell them that a zip is always pulled to open and close it. Put the zip into the sorting ring labelled 'Pull'. Note (or ask an adult helper to note) the children's responses. Now talk about the Velcro and ask the same question. If necessary, say that the Velcro is pulled to undo it but is pushed to fasten it. Put the Velcro into the sorting ring labelled 'Push and pull'. Repeat the activity with the other items in your collection. Talk about the sorted items.

ASSESSMENT ACTIVITY 2

Repeat the Main assessment activity with a different set of objects (including those used in Lessons 1–5), working with groups of four children. You may wish to set up an interactive display for them to use for a number of days after the activity, so that you can repeat the assessment a few days later with those children who did not quite understand the first time. With less able children, repeat the Main assessment activity with groups of four.

ASSESSMENT ACTIVITY 3

Place the items from Assessment activity 2 in the centre of a group of eight children. Explain the activity. Shuffle the label cards and hold up the one on top. Invite one child to find an item that matches the label exactly (for example, if 'Pull' is held up then the child should find an object that requires only a pull to work). Ask the child to explain his or her choice, and invite the rest of the group to say whether the child is correct. If correct, the child may keep the object. When the game is finished, count up the number of objects each child has. Place three sorting rings in the centre of the group and label them 'Pull', 'Push' and 'Push and pull' (tell the children what the labels say). Ask the children to put their objects into the correct sorting rings. This game can be differentiated in many ways. Make sure that more able children are left with more challenging and less obvious items to distinguish, including some that they have not explored before. Less able children could be asked to select from objects included in previous lessons in the unit.

ASSESSMENT ACTIVITY 4

Give each child a 'Push', 'Pull' or 'Push and pull' label. Ask the children to find an object in the classroom that works in that way. When they have done so, ask them to say why they chose the object they did. Tick the names of the children who are able to complete this activity.

Assessment outcomes

On completion of these Assessment activities, you should know which children have attained the following objectives linked to knowledge and understanding of the world:
● Can say whether familiar objects require a pull, a push or either to make them work.
● Know that the fasteners on our clothes need to be pushed, pulled or pushed and pulled to open and close them.
● Can sort familiar objects into three sets according to given criteria.

PLENARY

Together, make three lists of all the items identified in Assessment activity 4: one list of items that require a push, another list of items that require a pull, and a third list of items that work by either a push or a pull (or by both).

Name

Pull it on

Colour all the things that we **pull** on and **pull** off.

Name

Make a stick puppet

1.

2.

3.

4.

5.

6.

UNIT 6 FORCES & MOTION

Push me up, pull me down

Cut and stick.

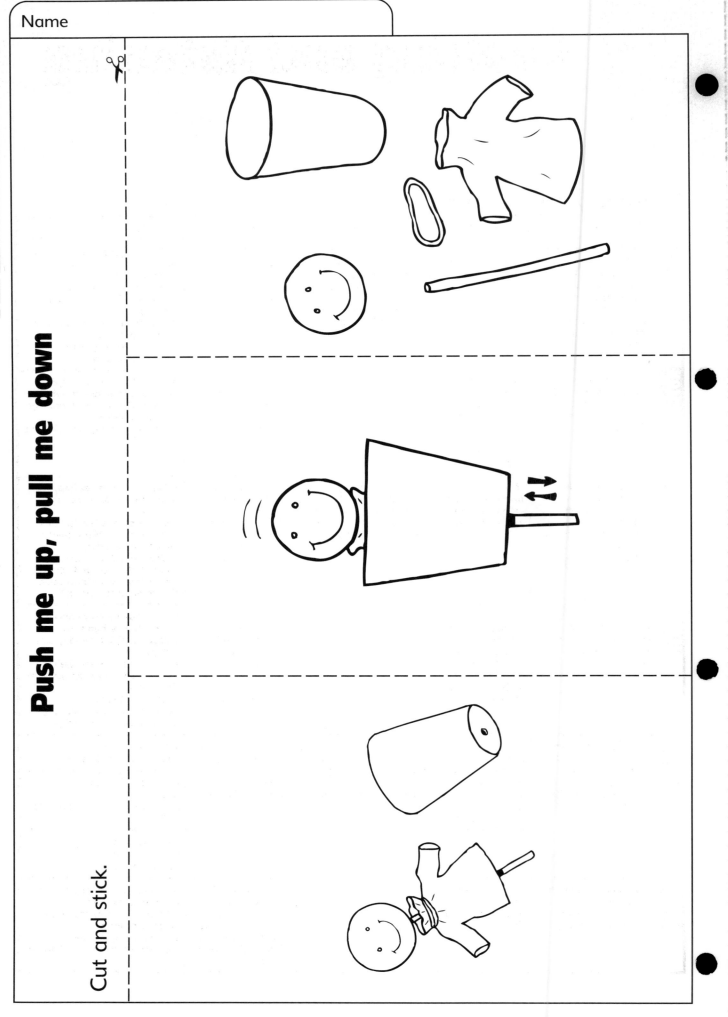

Looking and listening

ORGANISATION (13 LESSONS)

	OBJECTIVES	MAIN ACTIVITY	GROUP ACTIVITIES	PLENARY	OUTCOMES
LESSON 1	● To learn that there are lots of different colours in the world. ● To learn and recognise the names of familiar colours. ● To sort objects into sets of the same colour.	Make lists of objects that have familiar colours.	Make colour displays. Sort objects and shapes by colour, considering shades. Paint pictures of coloured objects. Make coloured, textured patterns from paper and fabric.	Sort the children's paintings by colour and add them to the display.	● Can recognise and identify familiar colours in the environment. ● Understand that there is a range of colours in the local environment. ● Can make simple recordings of their observations. ● Are developing early observation skills.
LESSON 2	● To learn that some things produce and give out light, and that these are called 'light sources'.	Explore light sources. Talk about things that give out light. Draw and find pictures of light sources. Play 'torch tag'.		Make a book of the children's pictures. Turn on the displayed light sources.	● Know that certain objects produce and give out light. ● Can make simple recordings of their findings. ● Are developing early skills in observation.
LESSON 3	● To discover what happens when two colours are mixed together. ● To learn that colours change shade when mixed with white or black.	Make patterns by mixing different amounts of red and yellow paint.	Make patterns by mixing different amounts of two primary-coloured paints, and by mixing white or black paint with a primary colour.	Talk about the shades and colours the children have made, reinforcing vocabulary.	● Can explore what happens when two colours are mixed together. ● Can explore what happens when white or black paint is mixed with a colour. ● Understand the terms 'darker', 'lighter' and 'shade'. ● Develop early observation and communication skills.
LESSON 4	● To discover that things seem to change colour when looked at through coloured cellophane.	Look at familiar objects through red, green and blue cellophane paper. Explore the effects of looking through this paper.		Talk about the colour of the same object when seen through different-coloured 'windows'.	● Can observe how various colours look when seen through red, blue and green cellophane. ● Can communicate their findings by talking about what they can see. ● Can develop their exploration skills by finding other objects to investigate.
LESSON 5	● To learn that some things are dull and others are shiny. ● To learn that when things are shiny, they reflect light.	Look for a self-image in a range of materials. Sort them into two groups and identify the materials that reflect as 'shiny'.	Make a mirror. Find shiny and dull objects. Look for a self-image in a range of metals. Blow bubbles and look for reflections.	The children talk about what they have found out when exploring metal objects and foils.	● Can carry out an investigation with support. ● Can record, by speaking and drawing, what they have found out. ● Are developing observation skills. ● Can select materials suitable for a given task. ● Know what is meant by 'shiny' and 'dull'.
LESSON 6	● To identify light and dark places. ● To learn how to make a dark place.	Find and make dark places. Talk and write about darkness.		Talk about the children's feelings when they visited the dark place, and what they could see.	● Can use their sense of sight to explore dark places. ● Know that darkness is the absence of light. ● Can investigate how blocking light forms a shadow.

ORGANISATION (13 LESSONS)

	OBJECTIVES	MAIN ACTIVITY	GROUP ACTIVITIES	PLENARY	OUTCOMES
LESSON 7	● To learn that it is more difficult to find an object in the dark than in the light.	Play 'Hunt the Thimble' in the dark place. Talk about how the thimble was found.	Play the game again in the dark, with a torch and in full light.	Talk about whether it was easier to find the thimble in the dark or with a torch.	● Know that it is only possible to see when there is light. ● Know that we use our eyes to see.
LESSON 8	● To learn that colours look different when it is nearly dark.	Explore the colour and shade of objects in bright light and in dim light.		Record which objects looked a darker colour and which looked the same.	● Know that light is needed to see. ● Know that colours can look different in near dark and in bright light. ● Can say what happened in an investigation.

	OBJECTIVES	MAIN ACTIVITY	ACTIVITIES 2 and 3	4 and 5	OUTCOMES
ASSESSMENT 9	● To assess the children's knowledge of a variety of colours in the world. ● To assess the children's ability to sort objects by their colour; change colours by mixing materials; identify objects that are dull and shiny.	Make coloured biscuits.	Make coloured icing. Ice the biscuits. Make jellies and talk about how they look.	Make and label sandwiches with coloured fillings. Make drinks and lay the table for a 'colour party'. Talk about how the food and drinks look.	● Recognise and name familiar colours. ● Identify things that are dull and shiny. ● Identify things that reflect light. ● Predict the outcome of mixing two colours.
LESSON 10	● To learn that we use our ears to hear.	Explore the sounds of a range of musical instruments. Make different sounds with drums and beaters. Make shakers.		The children demonstrate their shakers and talk about the sounds they make.	● Can make different sounds with the same instrument. ● Know that we hear with our ears. ● Can use the sense of hearing to compare different sounds.
LESSON 11	● To learn that different materials make different kinds of sounds. ● To explore different ways of producing high and low sounds.	Explore different wind chimes. Order them by how high or low a sound they make.	Sort instruments by whether they make a high or a low sound. Make wind chimes from a range of materials. Order the sounds made with musical triangles of different sizes.	Listen to the children's wind chimes. Link the findings with wind chimes to those with triangles.	● Can explore different sounds made with instruments. ● Know that longer tubes make lower notes. ● Can observe similarities and differences between different objects, including the sounds made with them.
LESSON 12	● To learn that sounds can be loud or quiet. ● To investigate how to make loud and quiet sounds using a range of materials.	Make sound effects to accompany one verse of a poem about the weather.	Make sound effects for all the verses. Paint pictures of the types of weather in the poem. Listen to a tape of the weather and identify the sounds. Listen to the sound effects on a computer story.	Perform the poem with the added sound effects.	● Can explore and change the sounds made with instruments. ● Understand what we mean by 'quiet' and 'loud' sounds. ● Can listen carefully to each other and work together. ● Know that we use our ears to hear.

	OBJECTIVES	MAIN ACTIVITY	ACTIVITIES 2 and 3	4 and 5	OUTCOMES
ASSESSMENT 13	● To assess the children's understanding of the different sounds made by musical instruments, and that sounds can be changed. ● To assess the children's ability to explore a range of sounds made by a variety of materials, and to identify objects from their sounds.	Listen to and identify sounds all around. Say whether they are loud, quiet, high or low.	Make sound effects to accompany a poem. Make different kinds of sound using a range of musical instruments.	Make a musical instrument from a range of materials. Draw it and name the type of sound it makes. Match unseen instruments to pictures.	● Know that we use our ears to hear and listen. ● Know that sounds can be changed. ● Understand the difference between high and low sounds, and between loud and quiet sounds. ● Recognise familiar objects by the sounds that they make.

Context: COLOURS AROUND US

The first nine lessons in this unit are all set within a colour theme. Although they are concerned with changing and comparing colours in paint, food and light, they first of all provide a context for developing enquiry skills. The first lesson can be developed over a number of days or weeks. The book *The Rainbow Fish* by Marcus Pfister (North-South Books) could be read with the children to introduce the topic.

LESSON 1

OBJECTIVES
- To learn that there are lots of different colours in the world.
- To learn and recognise the names of familiar colours.
- To sort objects into sets of the same colour.

RESOURCES

Main teaching activity: A large display board (or more than one) and surface(s); backing paper and drapes in a range of colours, including those of the rainbow; several cardboard boxes in different shapes and sizes; a few shapes in different colours; a sheet of A3 paper, a marker pen.
Group activities: 1. Paper, coloured pencils or crayons. **2.** Sets of coloured shapes and other coloured classroom objects; sorting rings; photocopiable page 169 (for assessment). **3.** Paper, paintbrushes, paints in a range of colours. **4.** Scraps of paper and fabric in a range of colours, including the colours of the rainbow, silver and gold; adhesive, collage materials.

Vocabulary
sort; the names of the colours in your collection(s)

PREPARATION

Cover the display board(s) with your chosen backing material. Arrange several cardboard boxes of different shapes and sizes along the top of the display surface, and cover them with matching fabric or paper.

INTRODUCTION

Tell the children that they are going outside to look for all the different colours that can be found in our world. Take them outside for a short session and ask them to look for different colours around them. Ask an adult helper to note down their observations for use in the Group activities and for the finished display. Ask the children which colours they can see most of outside. The answer will depend on your particular setting and the time of year.

MAIN TEACHING ACTIVITY

Gather the children around the display board(s) and talk about the colours that they have seen outside. Try to find an example of an object for each colour in your intended display. For example, you could include bricks, doors, television aerials, trees and leaves. Show the children one of the coloured shapes in your collection. Ask them whether they can think of something they saw outside that had the same colour. Make a note of their suggestions by drawing pictures on a large sheet of paper. Repeat this for a few other coloured shapes. Stop when you feel that the children understand the activity.

GROUP ACTIVITIES

1. Ask an adult helper to work with six children, continuing with the Main teaching activity above but asking the children to record their observations independently. They could do this by drawing pictures in the same colour on separate paper. The children's individual pictures can be stapled to the correct colour display at a later date.
2. Work with groups of six children in turn to sort coloured shapes and other interesting colourful objects into sets according to their colour. Talk about what other things have these colours. Can the children think of examples of things outside school that have the same colour? Discuss the different shades in the collection – for example, talk about the similarities and differences between the colours in the 'red' set.
 3. Set up a painting table and invite the children to paint pictures of some of the things they saw outside.
4. Set up colour tables (one table for each colour) and ask groups of children to use scraps of fabric and paper to make textured patterns to add to the display.

DIFFERENTIATION

Be sensitive to any children who are colour-blind, and only ask them to contribute to a colour display that they are able to discriminate.

With less able children, work with one colour at a time over several days or weeks. Reinforce the names and shades of the colours with this group, sticking to the more familiar colours: green, red, blue, orange and yellow.

More able children should be encouraged to think of things outside school that they did not see directly on the visit. For example, they can be asked to think about the colours of road signs and perhaps to suggest why certain colours have been used. (For example, warning signs and signs telling you to do something usually have a red border because this makes them easy to notice.) You may wish to move on to discussing simple logos on shop or restaurant signs.

ASSESSMENT

During the sorting activity, note those children who recognise certain colours reliably. Use a simple recording chart for this, such as the one on photocopiable page 169. Keep some of the children's work from Group activity 1 to show their knowledge of the range of colours found in the local environment.

PLENARY

Look at some of the children's paintings and talk about why particular things were chosen. Ask the children to which colour board each picture should be attached. Explain that you will leave the shapes and sorting rings out, so that the children can re-sort any shapes that accidentally get muddled.

OUTCOMES

● Can recognise and identify familiar colours in the environment.
● Understand that there is a range of colours in the local environment.
● Can make simple recordings of their observations.
● Are developing early observation skills.

LINKS

Between units: this lesson links with Unit 8, Lessons 2 and 4.
Across the curriculum: links are made with mathematical development through the sorting activity and the use of shapes. A pictogram or block graph could also be made to show the children's favourite colour. The textured colour sheets could be used to develop the children's sense of touch by encouraging them to explore different-feeling surfaces. Development of the colour theme into creative work is also possible. Over the next few weeks, add real items from the environment to the display; encourage the children to explore these using their senses.

LESSON 2

Objective	● To learn that some things produce and give out light, and that these are called 'light sources'.
Resources	A collection of objects that produce and give out light, including an electric lamp, candle, oil lamp, torch and overhead projector; a picture of the Sun; magazines with pictures of light sources; several torches of different types, spare batteries; paint and paintbrushes. Set up a surface to display the collection of objects.
Main activity	**NB** It is very easy to confuse young children if you go too deeply into explanations on what gives out light and what reflects light. For example, the Moon does not give out light directly but reflects light from the Sun. However, young children will not understand this principle, since we cannot see the Sun at night but we see better when the Moon is full. If children suggest the Moon as a light source, simply explain that it does not give out light but reflects the light of the Sun. Stars do give out light: our Sun is a star. I suggest that you refer only to objects that can easily be identified as giving out light: items that can be turned on and off (such as lamps and torches) and items that can be extinguished (such as candles). Should the children suggest objects that appear to give out light but technically do not, simply state that these are not light sources without trying to explain why. Show the torch and ask the children to tell you what its purpose is. Pass the torch around the group and ask the children whether they can make it give out light. Spend a few moments switching the torch on and off. Repeat the activity with the other objects in your collection. Look at the picture of the Sun. Ask the children how we can turn the Sun on and off. This question will allow you to assess the children's conceptual level of understanding regarding day and night. Some children may know that the Sun cannot be switched off and does not disappear: it is giving light to another part of the world. Organise Group activities with adult support: **1.** Ask the children to draw and paint pictures of things that give out light (are light sources). **2.** Ask the children to find pictures in magazines of objects which produce light. **3.** Let a group set up a shop in the role-play area, selling different kinds of torches. **4.** Play 'torch tag' with a group in a darkened room. Give each child a torch; they have to chase and 'tag' each other's light on the ceiling and walls.
Differentiation	In Group activity 1, ask less able children to draw pictures of things in the 'light source' collection only. Work with more able children to identify which part of the object actually gives out light, and which part is the energy source (for example, the bulb and battery respectively in a torch). Ask them to draw a picture of one item and to label the part that gives out the light.
Assessment	In Group activity 1, encourage the children to draw all the light sources they can think of. Use these pictures as a record of their understanding. There will, inevitably, still be children who draw the Moon when you have explained that it is not a light source.
Plenary	Talk about the children's pictures and the objects they have drawn. Use these to reinforce the learning objective and to iron out any misconceptions. Stick the pictures into a book to record what the children have done, and display this next to the collection of light sources for the children to look at. At some point in the day, make a special point of turning on all the light sources. Remember to turn them off when you leave the room.
Outcomes	● Know that certain objects produce and give out light. ● Can make simple recordings of their findings. ● Are developing early skills in observation.

LESSON 3

OBJECTIVES
● To discover what happens when two colours are mixed together.
● To learn that colours change shade when mixed with white or black.

RESOURCES
Main teaching activity: Red and yellow paint, a large sheet of paper, a paintbrush, water, a mixing plate.
Group activities: 1 and 2. Large sheets of paper, paintbrushes, water, mixing plates, several adult helpers (or organise the activities over several days); black, white, yellow, blue and red paint; small pots.

PREPARATION
Put the paint into little pots for the children to use. Either powder paint or ready-mixed paint will be suitable.

Vocabulary
shade, mix red,
black, white, pink,
orange, yellow,
green, blue,
purple, darker,
lighter

INTRODUCTION

Show the children the red and yellow paint. Explain that you are going to make a pattern on the paper by mixing these two colours together. Go through the procedures for mixing paint – for example, the need to wash the brush before putting it into a different colour (although, if you have lots of small pots of different paints, it will not cause too much of a disaster if the children forget in their excitement).

MAIN TEACHING ACTIVITY

Use red paint to make a shape somewhere on the large sheet of paper. Show the children how to wash the brush out thoroughly before using yellow to paint a yellow shape. Now take a little red paint and mix some yellow with this to make a different colour. Paint a shape with your new colour. Repeat this, adding different amounts of red and yellow paint to make many shades of red, yellow and orange, until the sheet is almost covered. If you wish, when you are sure that the children understand the process, you could invite a small group to help you paint the shapes.

GROUP ACTIVITIES

1. Set up six tables with paint in different colours. Three tables should have two colours (such as blue and yellow) and three should have one colour with white and black (for example, red, white and black). This will cover all the possible combinations. Talk to the children about whether they have made a darker or lighter shade as they mix the colours. Allow them to walk around and see the colours being made by the other groups.
2. Repeat the activity over a number of days, so that the children have the opportunity to mix different colours. Unless they have had first-hand experience of mixing a range of colours, their understanding of colour mixing cannot be assured.

DIFFERENTIATION

Be sensitive to any children who are colour-blind; allow them to work with colours they do not have difficulty in discriminating. Allow more able children to work on the tables with white and black, leaving less able children to mix two colours only.

ASSESSMENT

Question the children during the activity, asking them to predict the colours they will make when they mix each pair of colours. Ask them whether they will make a darker or lighter shade if they mix black with their chosen colour. Note those children who are able to answer or those who are not, whichever group is the smaller.

PLENARY

Talk about all the shades of colour the children have made. Create a colour-mixing poster to show which pairs of colours make orange, purple and green. Add the sheets to the colour displays created during Lesson 1. Reinforce the vocabulary 'shade', 'lighter' and 'darker' by finding out exactly what happened when white and black paint was mixed with each colour. How many new colours did the children make by mixing pairs of colours?

OUTCOMES

● Can explore what happens when two colours are mixed together.
● Can explore what happens when white or black paint is mixed with a colour.
● Understand the terms 'darker', 'lighter' and 'shade'.
● Develop early observation and communication skills.

LINKS

Across the curriculum: this lesson links to creative development. The colour-mixing theme can be developed through other topics. The story *White Rabbit's Colour Book* by Alan Baker (Kingfisher), in which a white rabbit jumps into a series of paint pots, is a useful stimulus.

LESSON 4

Objective	● To discover that things seem to change colour when looked at through coloured cellophane.
Resources	Red, green and blue cellophane; a collection of bright green, blue and red objects; three mesh bins, black sugar paper, cardboard tubes, pipe-cleaners, paper clips, adhesive, sticky tape, a kaleidoscope. Cut the cellophane into squares approximately 15cm × 15cm.
Main activity	**NB** The primary colours of light are red, blue and green, and the children will need to know this in Key Stage 2. Using only these colours at this stage will help to prevent later confusion. It is not necessary to explain why you have restricted the choice to these three colours. Give each child in the class a piece of red cellophane to look through. Ask the children to say what they can see. Repeat with the blue and green squares. Respond to any questions and remarks such as 'Look, it's changed colour' constructively, perhaps by asking another question such as *Look again without the cellophane. Has it really changed colour, or did it just look that way through the cellophane?* Explain that when we look through coloured glass or paper, things may seem to be a different colour. Organise Group activities with adult support: **1.** Cover three quarters of a window with green, blue and red cellophane, leaving one quarter plain glass, and invite the children to look at objects outside. Take suitable objects outside for them to look at through the window; they can also look at trees, cars and so on. What do they notice about the way that green, blue and red objects look through each of the colours? The red and yellow 'Crazy Coupe' range of wheeled toy cars are good for this, as they show very different colours when seen through each of the coloured windows. **2.** Cover three mesh bins with red, green and blue cellophane. Take three objects of the same colour and place one inside each upturned bin in the morning. Ask the children to guess the 'true' colour of the objects. Allow them to notice any changes that appear to take place when the objects are removed from underneath the bins at the end of the day. Each day, change the set of objects for a set with a different colour. **3.** Let the children make stained-glass windows by sticking coloured cellophane over holes cut in black sugar paper, then look through these and note apparent changes. **4.** Let the children make model telescopes from cardboard tubes and spectacles from pipe-cleaners, with coloured cellophane for the lenses. **5.** Leave several kaleidoscopes around for the children to explore.
Differentiation	Ask more able children to explore a range of objects that, when looked at through coloured cellophane, look a different colour. Ask them to decide which colour looked the most different through each type of cellophane. Some may be able to predict the changes (for example, it will look darker, greener and so on) before testing their prediction with the cellophane – but be prepared for them not wanting to risk being wrong. The skill of prediction is about maturity as well as ability. Encourage the children to use the language developed in the previous lesson. Use one colour only with less able children, developing the activity over a number of days or weeks. Choose objects that look darker and lighter when placed behind the chosen colour of cellophane. It may be appropriate for the children to make comments while wearing glasses with coloured lenses throughout the day. Note any children who are colour-blind, and allow for this during the activity.
Assessment	Note those children who are able to describe the difference between the colours of objects when looked at through different-coloured pieces of cellophane.
Plenary	Ask those children who are able to describe what they saw when they looked through the coloured windows. *What colour does the tree look when seen through the red, blue and green windows? What colour does it look when seen through the plain window? How many of you agree? Who thinks something different?*
Outcomes	● Can observe how various colours look when seen through red, blue and green cellophane. ● Can communicate their findings by talking about what they can see. ● (More able children) Can develop their exploration skills by finding other objects to investigate.

LESSON 5

OBJECTIVES

● To learn that some things are dull and others are shiny.
● To learn that when things are shiny, they reflect light.

RESOURCES

Main teaching activity: The story of 'Snow White and the Seven Dwarves', a mirror; a collection of polished and dull wood, various metal and plastic objects.
Group activities: 1. Various sheets of metal foil (see Preparation); plastic sheeting, hardboard, adhesive. **2.** Sorting rings. **3.** Large polished metal spoons, mirrors. **4.** Silver and coloured foils (see Preparation). **5.** Bubble mixture and blowers.

Vocabulary
image, reflection, bent, upside-down, mirror, dull, shiny

PREPARATION

Provide mirror-sized pieces of various good quality foils (at least 20cm × 20cm) for the children to stick onto pliable hardboard, thick cardboard or plastic sheeting. Make sure the foil has no creases. A good reflective covering, of the type used for car windows, will be effective for this activity (but expensive).

INTRODUCTION

Read the story of 'Snow White and the Seven Dwarves', showing the children a mirror at the appropriate point in the story. At the end of the story, ask the children whether they can see their 'reflection' in the mirror. Explain that this is also called an 'image'.

MAIN TEACHING ACTIVITY

Show the children your collection of dull and polished metals, wood and plastics. Pass the things around for the children to handle, and invite them to say whether they can see their image in the materials. Together, sort the materials into two piles: those that reflect an image and those that do not. Tell the children that the ones that show an image are 'polished' or 'shiny' and those that do not are 'not shiny' or 'dull'.

Compare the shiny things to the mirror. *Which is best for seeing your own image?* Elicit the response that the mirror is best. Now tell the children that Snow White's wicked stepmother has lost her mirror. *What can she do?* Tell the children that you want them to make a new mirror for the stepmother.

GROUP ACTIVITIES

1. Ask an adult helper to work with a group, each child making a new mirror for Snow White's stepmother from the materials in your collection. Provide a range of foils and different backing materials: plastic sheeting, hardboard and cardboard. Make sure that some of the materials are shiny and others are not. The children will need to select the best material.
2. Ask a parent to help groups of up to ten children to find shiny and dull things for a display. He or she should reinforce the vocabulary 'shiny' and 'dull'. You may wish to provide sorting rings for the groups to use when they sort the objects. Leave the sorted collection on a display surface for the children to add items to during the week.
3. Work with groups of six children, investigating how their image looks in a selection of metal objects – some with a flat surface and some with concave or convex surfaces. Include the pliable mirrors the children have made, as well as large spoons and ordinary mirrors. Explain that the reflecting material in a mirror is a thin layer of metal. Encourage the children to talk about how their image looks in the different objects. Ask them to draw a picture of the image they see in each of the things they look into.
4. Leave the coloured foils on a table and invite groups of six children to explore their image in these foils. Ask them to find out whether one colour is better than another, and whether any colour reflects a clearer image than the silver foil.
 5. Leave bubble mixture and a range of blowers for the children to explore. Ask them to look for reflections in the bubbles.

DIFFERENTIATION

In Group activity 2, ask more able children to sort the objects by material as well, using a Carroll diagram. The criteria should be: 'shiny', 'not shiny' (or 'dull'), 'wood', 'metal' and 'plastic'.

Less able children should be asked to collect just shiny items on one day and just dull items on another. Explore the objects with this group of children, giving them plenty of opportunity to handle the objects in each collection and to talk about the textures they can feel as well as what they can see.

ASSESSMENT

Note those children who choose the most reflective material to make their mirrors. To ascertain their conceptual level, invite more able children to explain why their image is upside down in some items. Some very able children will be able to say that it has to do with the light 'bouncing off' the mirror at different angles.

PLENARY

Ask the groups exploring the collection of metals and the coloured foils to talk about what they have found out.

OUTCOMES

● Can carry out an investigation with support.
● Can record, by speaking and drawing, what they have found out.
● Are developing observation skills.
● Can select materials suitable for a given task.
● Know what is meant by 'shiny' and 'dull'.

LINKS

Across the curriculum: this lesson links with the design technology aspect of knowledge and understanding of the world. The story of Snow White can be used as a starting point for language and literacy lessons, and for work on investigating the number 7 in maths.

LESSON 6

Objective	● To identify light and dark places. ● To learn how to make a dark place.
Resources	Several thick curtains or blankets, a tent or a large cardboard box (that two children can sit inside comfortably), fixing equipment such as pegs and masking tape, a torch, paper, pencils, an Allan Ahlberg story cassette (such as *Skeleton* or *In a Dark, Dark House*). Make sure that the 'dark places' you intend to visit are safe.

Main activity	Go for a walk around the school, looking for dark places. There is usually at least one cupboard that can be explored. On return to the classroom, ask the children to say which places were dark and to give reasons why they think this was. Explain that these places were dark because there was no light: all the light had been blocked out. Tell the children that you are going to make a dark place for them to explore. Use a large cardboard box, curtains and blankets to make a tent-like construction. (You may wish to use an actual tent with extra covers over the top.)
	   Invite the children to use torches to explore the inside of the 'tent'. Limit the time for this activity, to give everyone a chance. An adult helper (or yourself) should sit inside the tent with the children, both to talk about the darkness and to supervise behaviour. Another adult should help the other children to record (in pictures) how they made the dark place. They should then write a simple sentence to say what darkness is: darkness is when all the light has been blocked out.
	   Play one of the Allan Ahlberg story cassettes to those children who finish early and are waiting for their turn in the dark place. These stories have a setting that is in the dark, and also have predictable structures in line with the literacy Programme of Study for the Reception year.

Differentiation	Set up a play activity for more able children: to investigate shadows by creating hand puppets and simple stick puppets, using a projector and a white screen. Encourage them to create a shadow play. Less able children should be allowed to explore the dark place both with and without a torch. Work with these children in small groups to make their own dark place (as in the Main activity).
Assessment	Note those children who understand that darkness is the absence of light. This will become apparent following their comments as they enter and leave the tent. The Plenary session will give you an opportunity to target those children to whom you've not had the opportunity to talk to during the lesson.
Plenary	Gather the children together when they have all visited the 'tent'. Talk about how they felt when they first went into the 'dark place'. *Was anyone frightened? Can you say why you were frightened?* Ask some of the children to say what they could see when the torch was turned off and when it was turned on. Record some of the children's responses if you wish.
Outcomes	● Can use their sense of sight to explore dark places. ● Know that darkness is the absence of light. ● Can investigate how blocking light forms a shadow.

LESSON 7

OBJECTIVE
● To learn that it is more difficult to find an object in the dark than in the light.

Vocabulary
dark, light, shiny, reflect

RESOURCES
Main teaching activity: A dark place (see Lesson 6), a metal thimble (or similar object).
Group activities: 1–3. As for the Main teaching activity. **2.** A torch.

PREPARATION
Test your dark place to make sure that the thimble cannot be seen without a light.

INTRODUCTION
Play 'Hunt the thimble' with the children, so that they understand the game: you hide the thimble, they try to find it!

MAIN TEACHING ACTIVITY
Explain to the children that they are going to play the game while inside the 'dark place'. Hide the thimble inside the dark place. Pick two children on whom you can rely to explain well and accurately what they have done. Invite them to go inside the dark place, making sure that very little light enters, and to try to find the thimble. Tell them that they are going to do this without a torch. When they have found the thimble and rejoined the class, ask them to say how they found the thimble. *Which sense did you use? Did you use your sense of sight only, or did you use another sense to find it?*

GROUP ACTIVITIES
1. Ask the children to go inside the dark place one at a time and find the thimble, so that they all experience looking for something in the dark.
2. Accompany the children into the dark place two at a time. Ask them to look for the thimble again, but this time using only their eyes. They must not move about. After a very short time, turn on the torch and time how quickly the children are able to see the thimble. You may wish the children to record by drawing what they could see inside the tent when it was dark and when the torch was turned on.

3. Allow groups of four children to play the game again in the classroom (in the light).

DIFFERENTIATION
Ask an adult helper to accompany those children who may be frightened or who will not be able to report accurately how they found the thimble.
More able children could think about *why* they can see the thimble better when the torch is turned on. (Because there is more light available to be reflected from the thimble.)

ASSESSMENT
During the Plenary session, note (or ask an adult helper to note) those children who realised that the light enables us to see and those who have no understanding of this. It may also be useful to note those who claim that they could see the thimble in the dark. This again is a question of maturity as well as ability: the child may understand that we cannot see in the dark, but not want to appear 'wrong'.

PLENARY
When all the children have had a turn at looking for the thimble, talk about whether it was easier to find the thimble in the dark or when the torch was turned on.

OUTCOMES
● Know that it is only possible to see when there is light.
● Know that we use our eyes to see.

LINKS
Between units: this lesson links to Unit 8, Lesson 4 on day and night.

Objective	● To learn that colours look different when it is nearly dark.
Resources	A red square, a blue triangle, a green circle, a rectangle in any colour; a torch, a 'dark place' (see Lesson 6); an enlarged (A3) copy of photocopiable page 170. Make sure that the dark place will have enough light for the children to see the shapes. You may need to carry out the activity with the torch switched on.

Main activity	Talk to the children about light and dark. *How many of you like going out in the dark? Why not?* Explain that places look very different when it is nearly dark. For a start, everything looks gloomy and dark. Talk about the colours that the children saw outside the school in Lesson 1. Look at some of the pictures that they drew. Ask them what they think these colours will look like when it is nearly dark. Many will say that they will look darker. Explain the following activity before starting it.
	  Work with groups of four children inside the 'dark place'. Turn on the torch if necessary, depending on the amount of light. Show the children the red square and ask them what colour it is. When they have all answered, shine the torch directly onto the shape and ask them again. Did they get the colour right? Ask: *Does it look exactly the same, or is it a different shade of red?* Encourage the children to say whether the shape looks darker, lighter, brighter or duller. Open the doorway to the dark place at this point, and ask the children whether the shape looks the same colour. *Has the shade of red changed?* Repeat the activity with the other shapes.
	  Ask an adult helper to play the same game with other groups of children in another dark place, if one is available.

Differentiation	Be sensitive to any children who are colour-blind; omit the use of the particular colours they are unable to discriminate. With more able children, relate the activity to the vocabulary used in Lesson 3 by asking them to say whether the colours looked darker or lighter when it was dark and when it was light. Encourage them to decide which colour looked the darkest in the dark and which one looked the lightest – or did they all look the same shade? Less able children should repeat the activity from Lesson 7: they should be challenged to find the coloured shapes with and without a light. This will reinforce the learning objective that light is needed in order for us to see.
Assessment	Listen to the children's responses during the activity to judge their level of understanding. How many children built on their learning in the previous lesson and understood that if it is nearly dark, they will not be able to see anything clearly?
Plenary	Talk about what the children have discovered. *How did the colours look different? Did any colours look the same?* Record the children's findings on a large chart; an enlarged copy of photocopiable page 170 can be used for this purpose.
Outcomes	● Know that light is needed to see. ● Know that colours can look different in near-dark and in bright light. ● Can say what happened in an investigation.

Context: PARTY TIME

The activities in this Assessment lesson draw together the learning objectives of the previous eight lessons. You can also use it as a context to assess the children's knowledge and understanding of mixing and how forces change the shape of materials. Invite the children to come to school dressed in one colour (for example, all blue or all green) on the day of the party. Please check for food allergies before the children eat any food. Carry out a risk assessment for Assessment activity 3 during the planning stage.

ASSESSMENT

LESSON 9

OBJECTIVES

- To assess the children's knowledge of the variety of colours in the world.
- To assess the children's ability to sort objects by their colour.
- To assess the children's ability to change colours by mixing materials.
- To assess the children's ability to identify objects that are dull and shiny.

RESOURCES

Main assessment activity: Milk, food colouring, biscuit mix, basins, clean paintbrushes, oven.
Assessment activities: 2. Icing sugar; red, yellow and blue food colourings; chocolate powder; a large bowl, a spoon, droppers, disposable cups, round-bladed knives. **3.** Red, green, yellow and orange jellies; bowls, water, spoons, a cooker or microwave oven. **4.** Bread, margarine, sandwich fillings in different colours (including cress, cheese, cucumber, tomato and pickle), paper plates. **5.** Fruits, a sharp knife, a plate, a large bowl; blue raspberry cordial, blackcurrant squash, water, transparent plastic cups; a large table.
Afterwards: Lots of bowls, plates, cups, spoons and paper napkins.

PREPARATION

Make enough biscuit mix for the children to have two biscuits each. You may wish to make a set of different shapes, animals or people.

INTRODUCTION

Tell the children that the day has come to celebrate all the work they have done on light and colour. Explain that you are going to make lots of things to eat for a party later in the day. At the same time, you are going to find out all the things they have learned about light and colour.

MAIN ASSESSMENT ACTIVITY

Roll out the biscuit dough and cut it into interesting shapes. Pour some milk into four different basins and mix in red, yellow, green and blue food colouring. Place a biscuit shape on a plate in front of you and ask the children what colour it is. Show them the different food colourings and explain that they are going to use them to decorate the biscuits. Invite them to predict what colour the biscuit will turn if painted with the red, yellow, green or blue food colouring. Decorate your biscuit at this point and talk about whether their predictions were correct. Invite the children to decorate their biscuits. Place the biscuits in the oven to cook, then remove them before they turn brown. Give each child two biscuits.

ASSESSMENT ACTIVITY 2

Work with groups of six children at a time to ice biscuits for the party. Mix a large bowl of icing sugar and place the food colourings on the table with a dropper in each bottle. Give the children three disposable cups each. Invite them to ice their biscuits using three colours. They can use the cups to mix small amounts of the colourings. Talk about the colours they could make, referring them to the lesson when they mixed colours. Note those children who remember how to make orange, purple, pink, brown and green.

ASSESSMENT ACTIVITY 3

Ask an adult helper to make jellies with groups of six children, using a cooker or microwave oven. The helper should show the children the jelly before it is made, and ask them to say what colour it is and whether they think it will change colour when water is added. When the jellies are set and cool, the helper should turn them out and ask the children to think of words to describe the jellies, encouraging them to name the colour of each jelly and say whether it is dull or shiny. Can they see their reflection? Can they see through the jellies? Ask the helper to note any children who use the word 'transparent' in their descriptions.

ASSESSMENT ACTIVITY 4

Make sandwiches with groups of children during the afternoon. Invite the children in each group to choose a colour and to use sandwich fillings of that colour only. Ask them to label the plates of sandwiches by their colour.

ASSESSMENT ACTIVITY 5

Make a fruit salad for the children to enjoy. Mix some fruit-flavoured drinks. Talk about the colour of the water and the changes that happen when the cordial is added. Lay the table with the children, placing foods of the same colour together. Place the fruit salad and decorated biscuits in the centre. Before the party begins, talk about the things on the table that have been made by mixing colours. Can any of the children point to anything that reflects light? Ask the children to name all the things that are red, orange, yellow, dull, shiny and so on. Pour out drinks into transparent plastic cups, so the children can see the colour of each drink.

Assessment outcomes

On completion of these Assessment activities, you should know which children have attained the following objectives in knowledge and understanding of the world:
- Recognise and name familiar colours.
- Identify things that are dull and shiny.
- Identify things that reflect light.
- Predict the outcome of mixing two colours.

PLENARY

Enjoy the party food together!

Context: MUSIC AND DANCE

The last three lessons in this unit can be taught through the musical elements of the creative development area of early learning. You may wish to set up a music shop in the role-play area, so that the children can pretend to listen to and purchase CDs of various kinds of music and even buy musical instruments – it depends on how sturdy your nerves are! You may wish to develop some of the ideas through dance, both for creative development and for physical development. These lessons also develop the concepts taught in Unit 1, Lesson 9.

LESSON 10

Objective	● To learn that we use our ears to hear.
Resources	A copy of the song 'Oh We Can Play on the Big Bass Drum' from *This Little Puffin* compiled by Elizabeth Matterson (Puffin); a range of instruments, including four drums, four tambourines and a range of beaters (including a brush and a felt beater); cardboard tubes, empty pots with lids, dried pulses and rice, gravel, sand; paints or gummed shapes.
Main activity	Sing the song 'Oh We Can Play on the Big Bass Drum' (perhaps taught in a previous lesson), adding verses and instrumental accompaniment. Talk about the sounds made by the various instruments in the song: do they make loud, quiet, fast, slow, tinkly, banging or musical sounds? Give each child in turn a different musical instrument to play, asking the child to produce a given kind of sound (for example, a loud sound, a scratchy sound or a tinkling sound). Ask the children who are listening to describe the sound being made. *Which part of your body are you using to hear the sounds?* Challenge the children to listen carefully to all the instruments, then sort them into sets of instruments that make similar sounds. Ask them to label the sets according to the type of sound that they make. Organise Group activities with adult support: 1. Work with a group of four children, using a variety of drums and beaters. Ask them to find out how many different sounds they can produce. Ask an additional adult to work with a group of four children, making as many different sounds as they can with a tambourine. 2. Leave a range of materials for the children to make their own shakers. They should decorate the pots using gummed shapes or suitable paints. A parent helper could support this activity effectively.
Differentiation	Be sensitive to any children with a hearing impairment, as there may be certain sounds to which they are intolerant. With less able children, play a 'Follow my leader' game: beat the drum with a wooden beater and ask the children to copy your sound, then repeat with the other instruments in your collection. More able children should be encouraged to record their sounds in a simple pictorial score (see illustration).
Assessment	During the focused Group activities, note those children who are able to make a range of sounds by changing the beater or by using it differently. Note those children who talk about the sounds they have made using appropriate vocabulary. (Also see Plenary.)
Plenary	Ask the children to show and demonstrate their shakers to the class. Encourage them to say what materials they used and how they made each shaker, as well as describing the sound it makes. Use this opportunity for further assessment of the children's understanding.
Outcomes	● Can make different sounds with the same instrument. ● Know that we hear with our ears. ● Can use the sense of hearing to compare different sounds.

LESSON 11

OBJECTIVES
● To learn that different materials make different kinds of sounds.
● To explore different ways of producing high and low sounds.

RESOURCES
Main teaching activity: Wind chimes made from wood and metal in different sizes (to produce a range of notes, from low to high – make sure that it is evident which set makes the highest and which the lowest sound).
Group activities: 1. A selection of musical instruments, both pitched and unpitched. **2.** Metal tubing, wooden dowelling or wooden wheels, foil, paper, strips of plastic, string or shoelaces, drawing pins, scissors, paperclips. **3.** A selection of different-sized musical triangles.

Vocabulary
high, low, higher, lower, highest, lowest, sound

PREPARATION
Drill (or ask someone to drill) a hole right through the metal tubing, about 2cm from one end, big enough to thread a lace or string through.

INTRODUCTION
Listen to the wooden wind chimes together. Ask the children to think of a few words to describe the sound they make. Repeat the activity with the metal chimes. Explain that different wind chimes make different kinds of sounds: some make low sounds and some make high sounds.

MAIN TEACHING ACTIVITY
Ask the children to say which set of wind chimes makes the lowest sound, and which makes the highest sound. Put the wind chimes in order, from the lowest-sounding set to the highest-sounding set. If possible, hang them from a rail.

GROUP ACTIVITIES
1. Work with groups of six children, exploring a range of instruments to decide whether they make high or low sounds, or both. Ask the children to sort the instruments into two sets according to which type of sound they make.
2. Ask an adult helper to work with groups of four children, making wind chimes for the garden area (if you have one). They can hang pieces of metal tubing from strings attached to a piece of wooden dowelling; or cut spirals and strips of foil, paper or plastic and hang them close together from dowelling or a wheel.
 3. Put out a range of musical triangles and ask the children to explore the sounds. Challenge them to put the triangles in order according to the note they make, from the highest to the lowest. Do they notice that the biggest triangle makes the lowest note and the smallest triangle makes the highest note?

DIFFERENTIATION
Be sensitive to any children with a hearing impairment. Direct less able children in their exploration of instruments. Play a very high note on a glockenspiel and ask the children to play a high note too. Repeat the activity with very low notes and so on, until you are sure that the children can hear the difference between high and low notes.
Ask more able children to explore what sounds they can make with a glockenspiel. Can they produce a high note and a lower note? Can they find other instruments that make both high and low notes?

ASSESSMENT
Make a simple tick chart to record whether the children understand the difference between high and low notes. Put an asterisk by the names of those children who can discern the difference between notes that are quite close together on the scale: these children may be ready to develop their musical skills further.

PLENARY
Listen to the wind chimes that the children have made, and decide whether they make a high or a low sound. Relate the discoveries of the group working with triangles to the sounds made by different-sized tubes in the metal wind chimes.

OUTCOMES
● Can explore different sounds made with instruments.
● Know that longer tubes make lower notes.
● Can observe similarities and differences between different objects, including the sounds made with them.

LINKS

Across the curriculum: this lesson links with, and allows the children to attain, some of the early learning goals in the area of creative development.

LESSON 12

OBJECTIVES
● To learn that sounds can be loud or quiet.
● To investigate how to make loud and quiet sounds using a range of materials.

RESOURCES

Main teaching activity: A copy of 'The Weather Song' from *Tinderbox* (A&C Black); a copy of the weather poem on photocopiable page 171 (or find one of your own); a watering can, water, a large metal bin.
Group activities: 1. A selection of musical instruments. **2.** Empty cardboard tubes (such as Pringles tubes), empty crisp packets, gravel in a tray, resources from the Main teaching activity.
3. Paint in a range of colours, paintbrushes, paper. **4.** A commercial audio tape of the weather or other sounds. **5.** Computer read-along stories such as those published by Oxford Reading Tree or Sherston (*Naughty Stories*), which invite the children to add sound effects at appropriate times.

PREPARATION

Cover an area of floor with plastic sheeting.

INTRODUCTION

Sing 'The Weather Song' together, adding body percussion as an accompaniment.

MAIN TEACHING ACTIVITY

Read the poem about the weather on photocopiable page 171 to the children, and ask them what the first verse is all about. Talk about the sounds the rain makes. Invite the children to suggest a possible sound to accompany the first line. Will it be a quiet sound or a loud sound? Now look at the second line together and talk about the sound the rain may make. Can anyone find something to make a suitable sound to accompany this line? Read the third line of the poem and talk about the sound that water makes when it hits tin. Demonstrate this by emptying the water from the watering can into a metal bin, and listening to the sound together. Decide whether it is a quiet sound or a loud sound. Finally, discuss possible sound effects for lightning and thunder; emphasise that the thunder sound must be very loud.

> **Vocabulary**
> loud, quiet, soft, louder, quieter, softer, very loud, very quiet, sounds, effects, accompany

GROUP ACTIVITIES

1. Work with groups of six children in turn to develop sound effects for verses 2 and 3 of the poem on page 171.
2. Ask an adult helper who has watched the Main teaching activity to work with a group (this could be the less able group), adding sound effects to verse 1 of the poem. The helper should reinforce the language and concepts of loud and quiet sounds, and then supervise the group as they practise their sound effects in another area of the classroom or school.
3. Set up a painting table so that the children can paint pictures of the kind of weather described in one verse of the poem. Let each group choose which verse to illustrate, but encourage them to select different verses.
4. Allow groups of four to six children to listen to a commercial audio tape of the weather or other sounds. Encourage them to identify the sounds.
5. In pairs, the children can listen to stories on the computer and add sound effects at the appropriate prompts.

DIFFERENTIATION

Be sensitive to any children with a hearing impairment who may be intolerant to certain sounds. Less able children should attempt Group activities 2–5 above.
   More able musicians can begin to think about how to make their sounds gradually become louder as the wind gets stronger and the rain gets heavier. After this teaching input, leave them to work together to compose their musical accompaniments to the poem.

ASSESSMENT

In the Plenary session, listen to the children as they perform to hear whether they have successfully created loud and quiet sounds in the appropriate places.

PLENARY

Allow each group to perform their sound effects for each verse of the poem in turn. Perhaps you could organise a performance in assembly.

OUTCOMES

● Can explore and change the sounds made with instruments.
● Understand what we mean by 'quiet' and 'loud' sounds.
● Can listen carefully to each other and work together.
● Know that we use our ears to hear.

LINKS

Across the curriculum: this lesson links to the early learning goals for creative development, which include being able to recognise and explore how sounds can be changed. The children also have the opportunity to develop their knowledge and understanding of the world by carrying out simple functions on a computer.

ASSESSMENT

LESSON 13

OBJECTIVES

● To assess the children's understanding of the different sounds made by musical instruments.
● To assess the children's ability to explore a range of sounds made by a variety of materials.
● To assess the children's understanding that sounds can be changed.
● To assess the children's ability to identify objects from their sounds.

RESOURCES

Main assessment activity: A space in the classroom for the children to sit quietly, a large sheet of paper, a felt-tipped pen, a set of 'reward' stickers.
Assessment activities: 2. Copies of a 'sounds' poem, such as 'Sounds Good' by Judith Nicholls (in *Twinkle, Twinkle, Chocolate Bar* edited by John Foster, OUP); pencils; a selection of everyday objects. **3.** A selection of musical instruments. **4.** A range of materials for making musical instruments; scissors, adhesive sticks; photocopiable page 172, crayons. **5.** Photocopiable page 173, pencils, a drum, a wooden block and beater, a set of bells, a pair of maracas, a musical triangle, a rainstick; a box with a lid or fabric cover.

PREPARATION

Make enough copies of photocopiable pages 172 and 173. Write out the poem with spaces for the children to draw pictures (see Assessment activity 2), and make copies. Put the instruments to be used in Assessment activity 5 into a box with a lid or fabric cover. Make sure that you are not going to be interrupted during the Main assessment activity, and open the classroom window.

INTRODUCTION

Gather the children together on the carpet and explain that they are going to listen to the sounds around them in the classroom and outside. They will have to sit very still and listen for two minutes. Ask them to suggest one or two sounds that they are likely to hear. Have a set of stickers ready as rewards if appropriate.

MAIN ASSESSMENT ACTIVITY

Sit very quietly for two minutes, listening to the sounds all around. At the end, ask the children to volunteer one sound that they heard. Make a list of these on the left-hand side of a large sheet of paper. When you have exhausted the children's ideas, go through the list again and ask the children to describe each sound in terms of how loud or quiet, fast or slow, high or low it was. The children may be creative and come up with other describing words. List the describing words on the right-hand side of the paper.

ASSESSMENT ACTIVITY 2

Ask the children to provide simple sound effects to accompany a poem read to them by yourself or an adult helper. Ask more able children to draw their accompaniments as simple pictures above the appropriate words.

ASSESSMENT ACTIVITY 3

Ask groups of six children to select instruments and play a loud sound, a quiet sound, a high sound and a low sound, as well as scratchy, tinkly, musical and banging sounds.

ASSESSMENT ACTIVITY 4

Ask the children to choose from a range of materials to make an instrument. Ask them to draw their finished instruments and add suitable labels on photocopiable page 172.

ASSESSMENT ACTIVITY 5

Show the children the pictures of instruments on photocopiable page 173. Remind them of the names of these instruments. You may wish to remind less able children of the sounds that they make. One at a time, use each instrument to make a sound from within the box (so the children can't see) and ask the children to colour, number or tick the matching picture on the photocopiable sheet. Watch the children as they do this, and note those who are correct or incorrect (whichever group is the smaller).

ASSESSMENT OUTCOMES

On completion of these Assessment activities, you should know which children have attained the following objectives linked to knowledge and understanding of the world:
● Know that we use our ears to hear and listen.
● Know that sounds can be changed.
● Understand the difference between high and low sounds, and between loud and quiet sounds.
● Recognise familiar objects by the sounds that they make.

PLENARY

Invite two or three children to show, demonstrate and talk about the instruments they made in Assessment activity 4. Prompt them to describe the sound it makes in terms of how loud, high and long-lasting it is.

Colour recognition

✓ recognises
✗ names correctly

Name	red	blue	green	yellow	orange	purple	pink	white	black	brown	grey	silver	gold

Light and dark

Did the shape look the same colour in the light and when it was nearly dark?

Write ✓ for Yes and ✗ for No.

Name

The Weather

Can you hear the rain? Pitter! Patter! Pitter! Patter!

When it runs into a drain, Gurgle! Gurgle! Glug! Glug!

When it hits the old tin roof, Ting! Ting! Ting! Ting!

Thunder crashes and lightning flashes.

Can you hear the snow, Swishy! Swish! Swishy! Swish!

Falling softly to the ground? Thunk! Thunk! Thunk! Thunk!

Hear it frozen, crunching underfoot. Crunch! Crunch!

Hear it turn to water when it melts. Gurgle! Gurgle!

Can you hear the wind blowing through the trees? Whoosh! Whoosh! Whoosh! Whoosh!

Rustling the leaves and blowing them to the ground. Whee! Whee! Whee! Whee!

The Sun comes out, feel the heat. Phew! It's hot! It's hot! Phew! It's hot!

Lovely weather we're having this week.

How does it sound?

Draw your instrument here.

Use these words to describe the sound your instrument makes:

low   **quiet**   **soft**

        loud   **high**

Can you hear it?

Write the number or tick ✓ the picture when you hear the sound.

1.

2.

3.

4.

5.

6.

Up in the sky

ORGANISATION (8 LESSONS)

	OBJECTIVES	MAIN ACTIVITY	GROUP ACTIVITIES	PLENARY	OUTCOMES
LESSON 1	● To learn that there are many things in the sky, some of which never fall to the ground.	List and talk about some of the things that are found in the sky.	Draw pictures of things in the sky. Sort other pictures by whether the things are in the sky or attached to the ground. Play picture dominoes. Make a display of things seen in the sky.	Talk about the things that are seen in the sky at night and in the day. Make a display of things seen in the sky during the day.	● Know that there are many things in the sky: some that have been made by people and some that are there through nature. ● Can sort things according to simple criteria. ● Can record what they know by drawing.
LESSON 2	● To learn that rain and sunlight together can create a rainbow.	Create a rainbow. Talk about the colours seen and make a display. Blow bubbles and look at the colours.		Read the story of Noah's Ark. Talk about where the rainbow really is.	● Know that when it rains and the Sun is shining, a rainbow may appear. ● Can communicate what they saw in an investigation by drawing.
LESSON 3	● To learn that the sky looks different during the day and at night.	Make lists of things that can be seen in the sky in the day and at night.	Make a display of 'The night sky'. Look for pictures of the night sky in books. Make pictures and prints for a display.	Compare the displays of the sky in the day and the sky at night.	● Know that some things can be seen at night but not during the day. ● Know that some things can be seen during the day but not at night.
LESSON 4	● To find out that objects look different during the day and at night.	Compare photographs of the same outdoor scene taken in daylight and at night.	Make the components of day and night street pictures. Make models of cars. Match pictures to day or night scenes.	Make the street pictures. Discuss the differences in colour and shade. Add light sources.	● Can identify similarities and differences between two pictures. ● Can apply previous learning to a new situation. ● Know that objects look different in the day and at night.
LESSON 5	● To observe the changes that may occur in the sky during the day.	Look at the sky and talk about shadows. Remind the children never to look directly at the Sun. Groups draw pictures of the sky and play 'shadow tag'.		Compare the children's drawings of the sky at different times of the day.	● Can observe changes in the daytime sky. ● Can identify similarities and differences between the appearance of the sky at different times over the day. ● Can recognise and observe shadows. ● Can predict when they will see a shadow and when they will not.
LESSON 6	● To learn that the Sun can be dangerous and that we need to take care on hot, sunny days.	Look at and talk about a range of items used on hot sunny days. Make a list of items the children would need. Sort the collection. Find a picnic area.		Make a list of things we need to do on hot sunny days.	● Know how to protect themselves from the Sun. ● Know that it is necessary to drink plenty of water on hot days. ● Are learning to consider their own needs independently.
LESSON 7	● To learn that water apparently disappears on a hot day. ● To learn that water dries up or evaporates.	Watch as puddles disappear. Talk about the changes.	Order pictures to record the changes. Investigate how long it takes for different puddles, and water pictures in different places, to dry up.	Talk about where the pictures dried up quickly and where they did not. Consider the reasons.	● Know that on a hot day, water dries up. ● Can investigate, with support, how quickly water dries up on different surfaces. ● Can say what happened in an investigation.

ORGANISATION (8 LESSONS)

OBJECTIVES	MAIN ACTIVITY	ACTIVITIES 2 AND 3	ACTIVITY 4	OUTCOMES
● To find out what the children know about the sky and beyond.	Draw a group picture of all the things that are seen in the sky and beyond it.	Draw a picture of a rainbow, showing what the weather would be like. Draw group 'day and night' pictures. Talk about the changes.	Make posters showing the dangers of the Sun.	● Be aware that the Sun can be harmful to our health. ● Be aware of various things that can be seen in the sky. ● Know that some things in the sky can only be seen at certain times.

Context: DISPLAYS

The lessons in this unit are introduced and developed through a series of displays. This is a useful tool for teaching very young children about their world, especially if the theme cannot be linked to play or first-hand experience.

LESSON 1

OBJECTIVE

● To learn that there are many things in the sky, some of which never fall to the ground.

RESOURCES

Main teaching activity: A large sheet of paper, a felt-tipped pen.
Group activities: 1. Paper, crayons, wide adhesive tape, string. **2.** Pictures cut from photocopiable page 184, scissors, sorting rings. **3.** Dominoes made from photocopiable page 185.
4. Classroom play equipment. **5.** Collage materials; templates or sponge shapes of the Moon, the Sun, the planet Saturn, stars and clouds; white and yellow paint.
Plenary: A staple gun, thread.

PREPARATION

Cover the display board with light blue or grey paper, depending on the time of year, for an 'In the Sky' display. Make a large book for the children's pictures, using a card cover and wide adhesive tape. Photocopy page 184 and cut out the pictures. Photocopy page 185 onto card, laminate the sheet and cut out the dominoes. Parents or carers may be willing to lend or donate suitable objects for the display.

Vocabulary

Sun, Moon, star, planet, cloud, lightning, rocket, aeroplane, bird, helicopter, butterfly, balloon

INTRODUCTION

Talk to the children about the dangers of looking directly at the Sun. It is very important that they know that this can damage their eyes, and that they must never do this. Make a poster, if you wish, to show next to the display – and contrary to other good practice, make the message negative by starting with the word 'NEVER'.

MAIN TEACHING ACTIVITY

Discuss with the children all the things that they may see in the sky. You may need to negotiate some of the suggestions, as some very young children may not discriminate between things in the sky and things high up on buildings (such as television aerials). Make a list on a large sheet of paper. Establish that you are talking about things that are high in the sky and not touching the ground or a building.

GROUP ACTIVITIES

1. Ask the children to draw pictures of some of the things that are in the sky and not touching the ground or a building. Make a book of their pictures and hang it by the 'In the Sky' display for the children to enjoy (and to add to if they wish).
2. Work with the children to sort the pictures from photocopiable page 184 into things that are found in the sky and things that can be seen by looking up but are attached to a building or a person. Talk about things that can be seen in the sky and also on the ground, such as aeroplanes and birds. You may wish to discuss which things are in the sky through nature and which are made by people.
 3. Play the matching dominoes game from page 185, asking the children to match identical pictures of things that are seen in the sky. Talk through the names of the things shown: 'star',

'planet', 'Moon', 'cloud', 'Sun'. As the children place the dominoes, they have to say the name of the object in the picture they are matching.

 4. Ask an adult to help a group of children sort through the play equipment in the classroom to find models of things seen in the sky (such as birds, helicopters, aeroplanes, kites, balloons and star shapes) and add them to the display.

 5. Ask a group of children to make large pictures from collage materials of the Sun, the Moon, the planet Saturn, stars and clouds. Ask them to use Sun, Moon, planet, star and cloud shapes cut from sponge to print a design on the class book cover.

DIFFERENTIATION

Allow more able children to try Group activity 2 unaided to begin with. Discuss which sets they have placed certain items in. For example, where did they put the kite? Ask them to draw additional pictures to include in their sets.

Work with less able children on Group activity 3, and reinforce the message that all these things are seen in the sky.

ASSESSMENT

Group activity 1 serves as a good initial assessment task, as it shows the children's understanding of the things that are found in the sky. The discussions during Group activity 2 will give you an insight into the children's conceptual level.

PLENARY

Talk about the large collaged Moon, stars, Sun and clouds. Discuss whether we see these things in the sky during the day or at night. Staple the Sun and clouds to the display board; attach thread to the stars and the Moon, then hang these to one side to depict the sky at night. Add the items collected during Group activity 4.

OUTCOMES

● Know that there are many things in the sky: some that have been made by people and some that are there through nature.
● Can sort things according to simple criteria.
● Can record what they know by drawing.

LINKS

Between units: this lesson links to Lessons 6 and 7 in Unit 3.

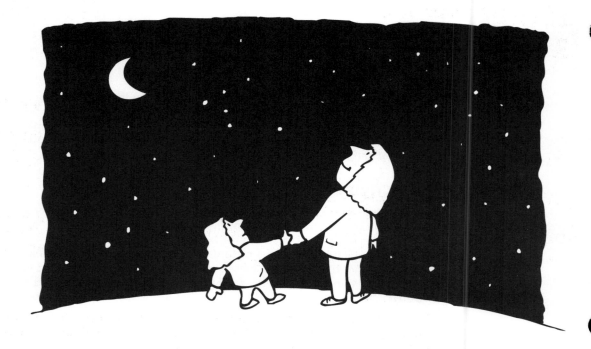

LESSON 2

Objective	● To learn that rain and sunlight together can create a rainbow.
Resources	*Apusskidu,* edited by Beatrice Harrop (A&C Black); a hosepipe attached to a tap, a large space outside, bright sunshine; a CD; squares of gummed and tissue paper in the colours of the rainbow, blue foil paper, scissors, a staple gun; photocopiable page 186, crayons in the colours of the rainbow; bubble mixture, blowers; a version of the story of Noah's Ark from the Bible. Make sure that you have the correct attachment to fit your hose to a tap that is close enough to your working space – this takes a lot of preparation, but the results are worth it.
Main activity	Sing the song 'I can see a rainbow' from *Apusskidu.* Take the children outside and stand them where they will be able to see the rainbow you are about to make. Stand to one side of the space and ask an adult helper to turn on the tap. As the water runs freely out of the hose, either turn on the spray mechanism or place your thumb firmly over the end to produce a spray of water. Lift the hosepipe into the air so that an arc of water is created. As sunlight goes through the water, a rainbow can be seen. Organise Group activities with adult support: **1.** Talk about the colours seen in the rainbow. The children may not have clearly seen all of the colours outside, and may need a prompt for some. Conventionally, it is accepted that the colours of the rainbow are red, orange, yellow, green, blue, indigo and violet (though the existence of indigo is doubted by scientists). Use a CD to reflect an overhead light: it will produce the colours of the rainbow. Together, make a large rainbow with paints or squares of gummed and tissue paper and staple it to the 'In the sky' display. Add raindrops cut from blue foil paper. **2.** Give the children a copy each of page 186 and ask them to draw the rainbow where the sunshine meets the rain. **3.** Repeat the Main activity with groups of eight children. This will give them an opportunity to see the rainbow more clearly, and to talk about what they can see. **4.** Put out bubble mixture and blowers. Ask an adult helper to blow large bubbles so that the children can see the colours on their surfaces clearly. Ask: *Are the colours the same as the ones you saw in the rainbow?*
Differentiation	Do Group activity 3 with less able children in smaller groups. Give them clues about what to look for by asking questions such as: *Who can see green, blue, red?* Give more able children a prism to look through, and talk about what they can see. Relate this to the colours seen in the water spray.
Assessment	Note those children who responded to what they saw by saying (or agreeing) that they saw colours in the water. This shows that they are beginning to communicate what happens during an investigation, as well as demonstrating their observation skills.
Plenary	Read the story of Noah's Ark from the Bible. Talk about why you have put the rainbow into the display. *Is it seen in the sky or on the ground?* Explain that although it appears to 'stand' on the ground, the rainbow is really hanging in the sky.
Outcomes	● Know that when it rains and the Sun is shining, a rainbow may appear. ● Can communicate what they saw in an investigation by drawing.

LESSON 3

OBJECTIVE
● To learn that the sky looks different during the day and at night.

RESOURCES
Main teaching activity: A picture of the sky at night (optional); a large sheet of paper and marker pen; pictures of the different phases of the Moon.
Group activities: 1. Silver foil, white paper, thread, grey paper, scissors, adhesive sticks.
2. A selection of story books showing the sky at night. **3.** White paint, chalk or pastels; black sugar paper. **4.** Sponge star and Moon shapes, white paint, strips of black paper.

Vocabulary
stars, Moon, shine, twinkle, bright, clouds, planets

PREPARATION
Cover a display board with black or dark blue paper. During part of the year, it gets dark early enough for the children to see the stars and the Moon before they go to bed at night. Write to parents and carers, asking them to support the activity by taking the children outside to see the stars and the Moon before they go to bed.

INTRODUCTION
Sing 'Twinkle, twinkle, little star' with the children. Ask the children whether they have ever seen the stars at night. *What do they look like?* You may wish to use a picture of the sky at night (available as posters and on bed linens) as a stimulus.

MAIN TEACHING ACTIVITY

Talk about what the children can see in the sky at night. (**NB** Take care not to refer to the Moon as a light source.) Make a list on the left-hand side of a large sheet of paper. Include stars, the Moon and clouds as well as anything else the children suggest, such as bats, birds and planets. Go through each item on your list and talk about its colour and its shape. This will lead to discussions about the Moon seeming to have different shapes at different times. Spend a few moments looking at pictures of the Moon and respond to any questions the children may raise. Explain that the Moon's shape appears to change depending on where it is in the sky as it moves around the Earth.

GROUP ACTIVITIES

1. Work with the children, making stars from silver foil and white paper. Attach white thread to some of these for mobiles. Make a large Moon from white paper, having decided with the children what shape it is going to be. Use grey paper to make several clouds. Add these to the display board to make a display of 'The night sky'.
2. Ask an adult helper to look through a selection of books in order to find and talk about pictures of the sky at night, the different Moon shapes and the stars in the sky.
3. Ask the children to make pictures of the night sky using white chalk, paint or pastels on black sugar paper.
4. Ask the children to use star and Moon shapes cut from sponge to print a border for the display, using white paint on black paper.

DIFFERENTIATION

Talk about nocturnal animals with the more able children, and include drawings of some of the ones that can fly in the picture. Some children will be keen to research the planets, as very able children often have a fascination with space. There are several books available containing good-quality pictures of the planets, from which the children will be able to draw pictures for the display.

Less able children could be led into the theme of the night sky by reading them a suitable story or poem.

ASSESSMENT

As the children make their stars in Group activity 1, ask them to talk about what they know about the night sky. As they refer to features such as stars, the Moon and clouds, add these to the display. Talk about things that can be seen at night at some times but not at others, such as aeroplanes, owls and bats. Note those children who know what things can be seen in the night sky.

PLENARY

Compare the two displays you have made so far. Look at the things that can be seen during the day, and then at the things that can be seen at night. Invite the children to name all the things that are in both pictures and all the things that are only in one.

OUTCOMES

● Know that some things can be seen at night but not during the day.
● Know that some things can be seen during the day but not at night.

LINKS

Between units: this lesson links to Unit 7, Lessons 7 and 8.

LESSON 4

OBJECTIVE

● To find out that objects look different during the day and at night.

RESOURCES

Main teaching activity: Two photographs of the same place, one taken during the day and the other at night; a copy of *Can't You Sleep, Little Bear?* by Martin Waddell and Barbara Firth (Walker Books).

Group activities: 1–4. A display board divided down the middle; templates of cars, houses, streetlights and people; squares of tracing paper, strips of grey or dark green paper, scissors, adhesive, paint in a range of colours. **5.** Recycled materials, adhesive, paints. **6.** Photocopiable page 187, pencils.
Plenary: A staple gun, squares and strips of yellow paper; templates of stars.

PREPARATION

Take two photographs of an outdoor scene, one by day and one by night, otherwise as similar as possible. Cover the display board so that the side representing daytime is a brighter blue than the side representing night-time.

INTRODUCTION

Read the story *Can't You Sleep, Little Bear?* and talk about how it gets dark at night-time. Ask the children what happens when it gets dark at home. *Do you switch on the lights? Why?*

MAIN TEACHING ACTIVITY

Show the children your two photographs and talk about the things that are the same and the things that are different. Talk about the time (see Unit 7, Lesson 8) when the children went into a dark place to look at coloured shapes. How many children remember that the colours looked darker or less bright? Ask the children whether they think the colours look the same at night or look darker. Remind the children how you made the colours look darker when you mixed black paint with them.

Explain that you are going to make a picture of the street where you live. Tell them about the houses in your street, the cars and the streetlamps. You are going to make two pictures: one to show what your street looks like during the day, and another to show what it looks like at night. The children are going to work in groups to make these pictures.

GROUP ACTIVITIES

1. Work with less able children to make a row of houses for the daytime picture. Explain that your house has a red front door and a neighbour's house has a green one. Ask two children to paint the correct coloured doors on two copies of the house template. When they have finished, talk about the colours of the windows during the day. If necessary, take the children outside to look. Stick the windows (squares of tracing paper) into place.
2. Repeat the activity with another group, making the colours of the doors darker by mixing a little black paint into the red and green paint. Invite four children to do the same for the four cars from Group activity 3.
3. Ask a group of four children to paint four cars for the daytime picture in yellow, red, green and blue.
4. Ask an adult helper to work with a group of eight children, making streetlights with thin strips of grey or dark green paper.
5. Ask groups of six children at a time to make models of cars from recycled materials. Ask them to paint the cars for either the daytime or the night-time picture.
6. Ask the children to complete photocopiable page 187 by drawing lines to match the objects to the picture (daytime or night-time) in which they belong.

DIFFERENTIATION

Work with less able children on Group activity 1. Ask more able children to paint pairs of people for the day and night pictures, using templates. The children must work together to decide on the colours of the clothes, and these colours must be repeated (but darker) for the night picture.

ASSESSMENT

During the Plenary session, invite different children to add to the display at different times. This will give you the opportunity to talk about the similarities and differences between the two pictures with small groups of children. Photocopiable page 187 can also be used to assess the children's understanding of the differences between how a street appears by day and how it appears by night.

PLENARY

With a group of less able children watching and helping, staple the cars, streetlights and houses onto the display board before talking about how the colours of the objects in the two pictures are different. Refer back to the children turning on their lights at night so that they can see. Show the children the squares of yellow paper and stick these to the night-time picture to show that the lights in the houses have been turned on. Now invite the children to say how the cars will look different at night. Invite another group to join you, and ask them to stick strips of yellow paper to the cars to represent the light coming from the headlights. Ask the children to say why the cars have their lights on. Ask another group to repeat this task with the streetlights, giving the ones in the night-time picture rays of light. Remove the stars and the Moon from the night-time picture on a copy of page 187 and add them to the night-time display. Invite these groups to go and make more stars for the sky, using the star templates. Work with the more able group to attach their people to the correct pictures. Ask them to give reasons for their decisions. Finally, add any further stars. Ask the children to place their models in front of the display.

OUTCOMES

● Can identify similarities and differences between two pictures.
● Can apply previous learning to a new situation.
● Know that objects look different in the day and at night.

LINKS

Between units: this lesson links with Unit 7, Lesson 8.
Across the curriculum: read rhymes and stories about night-time during literacy activities.

LESSON 5

Objective	● To observe the changes that may occur in the sky during the day.
Resources	Large sheets of paper; access to sunshine, shadows and clouds. Watch the weather forecast for a changeable day, or be ready to teach this lesson when the conditions are right.

Main activity	Talk about the sky on a 'normal' day: whether there are always clouds in the sky, whether the Sun is shining, whether the sky is blue or grey, and so on. Relate the discussion to the weather information you have collected in Unit 3.
	   Take the children outside and remind them about not looking directly at the Sun. Ask an adult helper to watch the children and make sure that they do not do this. Ask the children to stand with their backs to the Sun and look at the clouds in the sky. *What do the clouds remind you of? How much blue sky can you see between the clouds?* Talk about whether the Sun feels hot on their backs. *Can you see a shadow just in front of you? What does it look like? Is it as big as you, or is it smaller or bigger? Can you see any other shadows on the ground?* Go on a 'shadow hunt' if appropriate.
	1. Ask an adult helper to work with groups of six children in turn, drawing an accurate group picture of the sky as they can see it. They should decide how many clouds to add to the picture, and whether to show the Sun behind the clouds or in the middle of a blue area. The helper should number the pictures and write the time that each recording was made.
	2. Go outside with a group of ten children and play 'shadow tag'. When they are standing on a shadow, they cannot be tagged. If someone jumps on their shadow, they are 'it'.
	   Repeat the activities several times during the day.

Differentiation	Draw around the shadows of more able children and encourage them to observe how their shadows change size and position during the day. Organise the children into mixed-ability groups, so that less able children can be supported by other children.
Assessment	When the activities are repeated, ask the children to predict whether they will see any changes in the sky. *Do you think there will be more clouds? Why do you think that? Do you think you will be able to see your shadow?* Note the children's responses.
Plenary	Compare the group pictures, noting any similarities and differences. Invite the children to evaluate some of the observations: *Was Dave right? How do you know?* Ask them to watch the weather forecast later and predict whether the sky will be different tomorrow.
Outcomes	● Can observe changes in the daytime sky. ● Can identify similarities and differences between the appearance of the sky at different times over the day. ● Can recognise and observe shadows. ● Can predict when they will see a shadow and when they will not.

LESSON 6

Objective	● To learn that the Sun can be dangerous and that we need to take care in order to keep safe on hot, sunny days.
Resources	A collection of sun hats, parasols and sunglasses; sun cream; photocopiable page 188; paints, paper; a garden umbrella and base, cups, water.

Main activity	Send a letter home to parents and carers, explaining that you are setting up a display to show the dangers of the Sun and the need to take care on hot sunny days. Ask them to reinforce this message at home.
	  Look at the sunglasses and talk about how they are different from ordinary spectacles. Point out the darker lenses, and explain that these are special glasses for helping to protect the eyes. Emphasise that it is still not safe to look at the Sun even when wearing sunglasses: they are not that good at protecting the eyes. Talk about the other things in your collection. *Why do we put sun cream on? Why is it important to wear a sun hat? Why do we need to drink plenty of water in hot weather?*
	  Organise Group activities with adult support:
	1. Ask the group, working together, to list all the things that they need to do to keep safe on a hot day, using the writing frame on photocopiable page 188.
	2. Ask the children to arrange the collection of items on a display surface, grouping items of the same kind together.
	3. Set up a painting table and ask the children to paint pictures of the things they like to do on sunny days.
	4. Go outside on a hot day and find a shady spot for storytelling or a picnic lunch. Make the preparations first: wearing sun hats, putting on sun cream and so on.
	5. Set up a garden umbrella and resources for a play picnic (including cups of water) for the children to access.

Differentiation	Invite more able children to write individual lists of dos and don'ts for hot sunny days. The pictures around the writing frame will give them some clues. Ask less able children to draw pictures of the things that should and should not do.
Assessment	Use the children's lists of dos and don'ts to assess their understanding of what they need to use to protect themselves from the Sun. Note those children who have a good awareness of the issues; reinforce the message individually every day with those who do not.
Plenary	Make a list of all the things we have to remember to do on hot sunny days. You may think it appropriate to list all the things that the children should not do: stay in the sunlight for too long, stay thirsty and so on. Display the list(s) prominently by your display.
Outcomes	● Know how to protect themselves from the Sun. ● Know that it is necessary to drink plenty of water on hot days. ● Are learning to consider their own needs independently.

Context: SUMMER RAIN

The idea for the following lesson was inspired by watching the playground dry up quickly on a wet day under the strong rays of the summer Sun. The view is magnificent and exciting. Much discussion of where the water is going can take place, allowing you to challenge the more able thinkers without confusing the other children. As far as some children are concerned, if they can't see the water any more then it doesn't exist.

LESSON 7

OBJECTIVES

● To learn that water apparently disappears on a hot day.
● To learn that water dries up or evaporates.

RESOURCES

Main teaching activity: A hot sunny day, two half-litre containers of water, chalk.
Group activities: 1. Photocopiable page 189, scissors, adhesive sticks, paper. **2.** Water, cups, chalk, a broom. **3 and 4.** Paintbrushes, pots of water.

Vocabulary

dry up, evaporate

PREPARATION

Watch the weather forecast and choose a hot, sunny day.

INTRODUCTION

Ask the children to tell you what happens to an ice cream on a hot day. What about an ice lolly? When you are sure the children realise that these things melt because of the heat of the Sun, tell them that the Sun also makes something happen to water. Explain that you are going to explore what happens to water on a hot day.

MAIN TEACHING ACTIVITY

Go outside on a hot day and pour half a litre of water to make a puddle in the middle of the playground. Wait for the water to soak into the ground before drawing around the outside with a piece of chalk. Ask an adult helper to pour another half-litre of water to make a puddle in another part of the playground with a different group of children, and to draw around the edge of this puddle. After a while, return to the puddles to see whether anything has happened. What do the children notice about the size of the puddles? Draw round the puddles again. Repeat this action until the puddles have both dried up.

Back in the classroom, talk to the children to find out what they think has happened to the water. How many of them think the puddle has disappeared completely, and how many that it has dried up? Explain that the water has *dried up* or *evaporated*. It has become part of the air and gone up into the sky.

GROUP ACTIVITIES

1. Give the children a copy each of photocopiable page 189. Ask them to cut out the three pictures and put them in the correct order to show the changes they have just seen, then stick them down on paper as a record.
2. With a group, set up an investigation to compare whether a deeper puddle dries up faster than one that has been spread out. Tell them that they should use the same amount of water to make two puddles, then spread out one of the puddles with a broom.
3. Give the children pots of water and let them go outside and paint pictures. Invite them to work with their friends, starting at the same time, to paint similar-sized pictures on the bricks, paving slabs and playground. Challenge them to find out on which surface the picture dries up the fastest.
4. Challenge the children to find a place where their picture does not dry up too quickly.

DIFFERENTIATION

Begin to talk about fair testing with more able children. When you set up Group activity 2, ask them to think of a reason why you are going to use the same amount of water for each puddle. Let less able children explore this activity, rather than carry out a structured investigation. They should learn that on a hot day, water dries up.

ASSESSMENT

Keep the ordered pictures as evidence of the children's knowledge of how the puddle dried up.

Name

Day or night?

What to do on sunny days

1.

2.

3.

4.

5.

What happened?

Early learning goals: England

	Unit 1: Ourselves This is me!	Unit 2: Animals & plants Looking at animals and plants
● investigate objects and materials using all their senses as appropriate	1, 2, 3, 4, 6, 7, 8, 10	12, 15
● find out about and identify some features of living things, objects and events they observe	1, 2, 3, 4, 6, 7, 8, 9, 10, 11, 12, 18	2, 3, 4, 5, 8, 11, 15 16, 17, 18
● ask questions about why things happen and how things work		
● look closely at similarities and differences, patterns and change	1, 2, 3, 4, 9, 13, 14, 15, 16, 17, 18	1, 2, 4, 8, 13, 14, 15, 16, 17, 18
● be aware of change and its effects on them, for example their growth, changes in the weather, trees and flowers	5, 13, 14, 17, 18	6, 7, 10, 14, 18
● talk about their observations, make simple predictions	8, 12	

Curriculum framework: Scotland

	Unit 1: Ourselves This is me!	Unit 2: Animals & plants Looking at animals and plants
● develop their powers of observation using their senses	1, 2, 3, 4, 6, 7, 8, 10	12, 15
● find out about and identify some features of living things, objects and events they observe	1, 2, 3, 4, 6, 7, 8, 9, 10, 11, 12, 18	2, 3, 4, 5, 8, 11, 15 16, 17, 18
● recognise objects by sight, sound, touch, smell and taste	1, 2, 3, 4, 7, 8, 9, 10, 11	
● recognise patterns, shapes and colours in the world around them		2, 15, 16, 17, 18
● ask questions, experiment, design and make, and solve problems		
● look closely at similarities and differences, patterns and change	1, 2, 3, 4, 9, 13, 14, 15, 16, 17, 18	1, 2, 4, 8, 13, 14, 15, 16, 17, 18
● be aware of change and its effects on them, for example their growth, changes in the weather, trees and flowers	5, 13, 14, 17, 18	6, 7, 10, 14, 18
● understand some properties of materials	2, 8	
● sort and categorise things into groups	1, 2, 5, 6, 14, 17	1, 2, 4, 11, 15
● talk about their observations, make simple predictions	8, 12	
● care for living things, such as plants and pets at home		5, 9
● become familiar with the early years setting and places in the local area		

Desirable outcomes: Wales

	Unit 1: Ourselves This is me!	Unit 2: Animals & plants Looking at animals and plants
● investigate objects and materials using all their senses as appropriate	1, 2, 3, 4, 6, 7, 8, 10	12, 15
● find out about and identify some features of living things, objects and events they observe	1, 2, 3, 4, 6, 7, 8, 9, 10, 11, 12, 18	2, 3, 4, 5, 8, 11, 15 16, 17, 18
● ask questions about why things happen and how things work		
● look closely at similarities and differences, patterns and change	1, 2, 3, 4, 9, 13, 14, 15, 16, 17, 18	1, 2, 4, 8, 13, 14, 15, 16, 17, 18
● be aware of change and its effects on them, for example their growth, changes in the weather, trees and flowers	5, 13, 14, 17, 18	6, 7, 10, 14, 18
● begin to appreciate the differences in and the use of a range of materials	2, 8	
● talk about their observations, make simple predictions	8, 12	
● begin to appreciate the importance of the environment		5, 9
● have a basic understanding of the seasons and their features		

Northern Ireland Early Years Curriculum

	Unit 1: Ourselves This is me!	Unit 2: Animals & plants Looking at animals and plants
● investigate objects and materials using all their senses as appropriate	1, 2, 3, 4, 6, 7, 8, 10	12, 15
● find out about and identify some features of living things, objects and events they observe	1, 2, 3, 4, 6, 7, 8, 9, 10, 11, 12, 18	2, 3, 4, 5, 8, 11, 15 16, 17, 18
● explore a variety of materials, appreciating colour, shape, texture and sound	1, 2, 3, 4, 7, 8, 9, 10, 11	
● ask questions about why things happen and why they work		
● look closely at similarities and differences, patterns and change	1, 2, 3, 4, 9, 13, 14, 15, 16, 17, 18	1, 2, 4, 8, 13, 14, 15, 16, 17, 18
● be aware of change and its effects on them, for example their growth, changes in the weather, trees and flowers	5, 13, 14, 17, 18	6, 7, 10, 14, 18
● talk about their observations, make simple predictions	8, 12	
● begin to recognise parts of the body	7, 12	
● learn to treat living things and the environment with respect, care and concern and handle them sensitively		5, 9
● begin to identify a variety of sounds		

Unit 3: The environment The need for care	Unit 4: Materials What are materials?	Unit 5: Electricity Electricity around us	Unit 6: Forces & motion Exploring pushing and pulling	Unit 7: Light & sound Light and dark, loud and quiet	Unit 8: Earth & beyond Looking up
10	1, 2, 3, 4, 5, 6, 7, 8, 9, 10, 11, 12		1, 2, 3, 4, 5, 6, 7, 8, 9, 10	5, 6, 7, 8, 9, 10, 11	1, 2, 7
	1, 2, 3, 4, 5, 6, 7, 8, 9, 10, 11, 12			1, 2, 3, 4, 5, 6, 7, 8, 9, 10, 11	1, 2, 3, 4
	4, 5, 6, 7, 8, 9, 10, 11, 12	2, 3, 4, 5, 6, 7	1, 2, 3, 4, 5, 6, 7, 8, 9, 10	1, 2, 4, 5, 6, 7, 8, 9, 10, 11	5, 6, 7, 8
6, 7, 8, 9, 10	3		7, 8, 9, 10	4, 5, 6, 8, 9, 10, 11	2, 3, 4
6, 7, 8, 9	4, 5, 6, 7, 8, 9, 10, 11, 12				
	4, 5, 6, 7, 8, 9, 10, 11, 12	3, 4, 5, 6	1, 2, 3, 4, 5, 6, 7, 8, 9, 10	8, 9	

Unit 3: The environment The need for care	Unit 4: Materials What are materials?	Unit 5: Electricity Electricity around us	Unit 6: Forces & motion Exploring pushing and pulling	Unit 7: Light & sound Light and dark, loud and quiet	Unit 8: Earth & beyond Looking up
10	1, 2, 3, 4, 5, 6, 7, 8, 9, 10, 11, 12		1, 2, 3, 4, 5, 6, 7, 8, 9, 10	5, 6, 7, 8, 9, 10, 11	1, 2, 7
	1, 2, 3, 4, 5, 6, 7, 8, 9, 10, 11, 12			1, 2, 3, 4, 5, 6, 7, 8, 9, 10, 11	1, 2, 3, 4
	1, 2, 3				
					1, 2, 3, 4
	4, 5, 6, 7, 8, 9, 10, 11, 12	2, 3, 4, 5, 6, 7	1, 2, 3, 4, 5, 6, 7, 8, 9, 10	1, 2, 4, 5, 6, 7, 8, 9, 10, 11	5, 6, 7, 8
6, 7, 8, 9, 10	3		7, 8, 9, 10	4, 5, 6, 8, 9, 10, 11	2, 3, 4
6, 7, 8, 9	4, 5, 6, 7, 8, 9, 10, 11, 12				
	1, 2, 3		7, 8, 9		
12		2, 3, 4		1, 9	
	4, 5, 6, 7, 8, 9, 10, 11, 12	3, 4, 5, 6	1, 2, 3, 4, 5, 6, 7, 8, 9, 10	8, 9	
1, 2, 3, 4, 11, 12					
1, 2, 3, 11					

Unit 3: The environment The need for care	Unit 4: Materials What are materials?	Unit 5: Electricity Electricity around us	Unit 6: Forces & motion Exploring pushing and pulling	Unit 7: Light & sound Light and dark, loud and quiet	Unit 8: Earth & beyond Looking up
10	1, 2, 3, 4, 5, 6, 7, 8, 9, 10, 11, 12		1, 2, 3, 4, 5, 6, 7, 8, 9, 10	5, 6, 7, 8, 9, 10, 11	1, 2, 7
	1, 2, 3, 4, 5, 6, 7, 8, 9, 10, 11, 12			1, 2, 3, 4, 5, 6, 7, 8, 9, 10, 11	1, 2, 3, 4
	4, 5, 6, 7, 8, 9, 10, 11, 12	2, 3, 4, 5, 6, 7	1, 2, 3, 4, 5, 6, 7, 8, 9, 10	1, 2, 4, 5, 6, 7, 8, 9, 10, 11	5, 6, 7, 8
6, 7, 8, 9, 10	3		7, 8, 9, 10	4, 5, 6, 8, 9, 10, 11	2, 3, 4
6, 7, 8, 9	4, 5, 6, 7, 8, 9, 10, 11, 12				
	1, 2, 3		7, 8, 9		
	4, 5, 6, 7, 8, 9, 10, 11, 12	3, 4, 5, 6	1, 2, 3, 4, 5, 6, 7, 8, 9, 10	8, 9	
1, 2, 3, 4, 11, 12					
7, 8					

Unit 3: The environment The need for care	Unit 4: Materials What are materials?	Unit 5: Electricity Electricity around us	Unit 6: Forces & motion Exploring pushing and pulling	Unit 7: Light & sound Light and dark, loud and quiet	Unit 8: Earth & beyond Looking up
10	1, 2, 3, 4, 5, 6, 7, 8, 9, 10, 11, 12		1, 2, 3, 4, 5, 6, 7, 8, 9, 10	5, 6, 7, 8, 9, 10, 11	1, 2, 7
	1, 2, 3, 4, 5, 6, 7, 8, 9, 10, 11, 12			1, 2, 3, 4, 5, 6, 7, 8, 9, 10, 11	1, 2, 3, 4
	1, 2, 3				
	4, 5, 6, 7, 8, 9, 10, 11, 12	2, 3, 4, 5, 6, 7	1, 2, 3, 4, 5, 6, 7, 8, 9, 10	1, 2, 4, 5, 6, 7, 8, 9, 10, 11	5, 6, 7, 8
6, 7, 8, 9, 10	3		7, 8, 9, 10	4, 5, 6, 8, 9, 10, 11	2, 3, 4
6, 7, 8, 9	4, 5, 6, 7, 8, 9, 10, 11, 12				
	4, 5, 6, 7, 8, 9, 10, 11, 12	3, 4, 5, 6	1, 2, 3, 4, 5, 6, 7, 8, 9, 10	8, 9	
10					

Series topic map

Year/Primary	YR/P1	Y1/P2	Y2/P3	Y3/P4	Y4/P5	Y5/P6	Y6/P7
Unit 1: Ourselves	This is me!	Me and my body	Keeping healthy	Teeth and food	How I move	Growing up healthy	New beginnings
Unit 2: Animals & plants	Looking at animals and plants	Growing and caring	Growing up	The needs of plants and animals	Different sorts of skeletons	Life cycles	Variation
Unit 3: The environment	Out and about	Environments and living things	Life in habitats	How the environment affects living things	Habitats and food chains	Water and the environment	The living world
Unit 4: Materials	Exploring materials	Properties of materials	Materials and change	Natural & manufactured materials	Warm liquids, cool solids	Gases, solids and liquids	Reversible and non-reversible changes
Unit 5: Electricity	Making things work	Using and misusing electricity	Making circuits	Electricity and communication	Switches and conduction	Making and using electricity	Changing circuits
Unit 6: Forces & motion	Pushing and pulling	Introducing forces	Making things move	Magnets and springs	Friction	Exploring forces and their effects	Forces and action
Unit 7: Light & sound	Looking and listening	Sources of light and sound	Properties and uses	Sources and effects	Travelling and reflecting	Bending light and changing sound	Light and sound around us
Unit 8: Earth & beyond	Up in the sky	Stargazing	The Sun and the seasons	The Sun and shadows	The Sun and stars	Sun, Moon and Earth	The Solar System